THE BOOKMARK READING PROGRAM

PRIMARY READERS

Margaret Early, Elizabeth K. Cooper, Nancy Santeusanio, Marian Adell

Ring Around
the World

HARCOURT BRACE JOVANOVICH, INC.

New York   Chicago   San Francisco   Atlanta   Dallas

ACKNOWLEDGMENTS: For permission to reprint copyrighted material, grateful acknowledgment is made to the following:

THE BOBBS-MERRILL COMPANY, INC.: "Miguel and the Baker" adapted from *Folk Tales of Latin America*, adapted by Shirlee P. Newman, copyright © 1962, by The Bobbs-Merrill Company, Inc.

BRANDT & BRANDT: "Daniel Boone 1735–1820" from *A Book of Americans* by Rosemary and Stephen Vincent Benét, published by Holt, Rinehart and Winston, Inc., copyright, 1933, by Rosemary and Stephen Vincent Benét; copyright renewed © 1961, by Rosemary Carr Benét.

COMMUNICATIONS ADVISORS, INC.: "Apartment House" by Gerald Raftery from *The New York Sun*.

COWARD-MCCANN, INC.: Adapted excerpt from *Pilgrim Thanksgiving* by Wilma Pitchford Hays and Leonard Weisgard, copyright © 1955 by Wilma Pitchford Hays and Leonard Weisgard.

FUNK & WAGNALLS, N.Y.: "The Cattle Egret" adapted from *When The Stones Were Soft* by Eleanor B. Heady, copyright © 1968 by Eleanor B. Heady.

HARCOURT BRACE JOVANOVICH, INC.: "Watching the full moon," "Above the ruins," "My horse clip-clopping," and "Night over the pond" from *Cricket Songs: Japanese Haiku* translated and © 1964 by Harry Behn. Adaptation of "Lost in the Big Woods" from *Story Plays for Oral Reading* by Douglas and Margaret Rector, copyright © 1970 by Harcourt Brace Jovanovich, Inc. Dictionary definitions from *The Harcourt Brace School Dictionary*, copyright © 1968 by Harcourt Brace Jovanovich, Inc. HARCOURT BRACE JOVANOVICH, INC., and WM. COLLINS SONS & CO. LTD.: "Inoke Sails the South Seas" by Ronald Rose, text abridged and illustrations reproduced from *Inoke Sails the South Seas*, © 1966, by Ronald Rose.

HAWTHORN BOOKS, INC., 70 FIFTH AVENUE, N.Y.: Adaptation of *A Little Happy Music* by Robert Winsor, copyright © 1969 by Robert Winsor.

HORWITZ GROUP BOOKS PTY. LTD.: "Jets" from *One Sunday Morning Early* by Irene Gough. Published by Ure Smith, Sydney, Australia.

JACK AND JILL: "Operation Rescue" by Margaret Leach Eastman adapted from *Jack and Jill*, January 1965, © 1964 The Curtis Publishing Company.

J. B. LIPPINCOTT COMPANY: Adaptation of *The Horse Who Had His Picture in the Paper* by Phyllis McGinley. Illustrations by Helen Stone. Copyright, 1951, by Phyllis McGinley and Helen Stone. "Ring Around the World" from the book *All Through the Year* by Annette Wynne, copyright, 1932, renewal, ©, 1960 by Annette Wynne. "Indian Children" from the book *For Days and Days* by Annette Wynne, copyright, 1919, by J. B. Lippincott Company; renewal, 1947, by Annette Wynne.

LITTLE, BROWN AND COMPANY: Adaptation of "The Old Woman and the Tramp" from *Favorite Fairy Tales Told In Sweden* by Virginia Haviland, text copyright © 1966 by Virginia Haviland. Adaptation of "The Jolly Tailor Who Became King" from *Favorite Fairy Tales Told in Poland* by Virginia Haviland, text copyright © 1963 by Virginia Haviland. "Every Time I Climb a Tree" from *Every Time I Climb a Tree* by David McCord, copyright © 1952 by David McCord.

THOMAS NELSON, INC.: Adaptation of "The Case of the Rubber Pillow" from *Encyclopedia Brown Finds the Clues*, © 1966, Donald J. Sobol.

W. W. NORTON & COMPANY, INC.: "The Two Cats" from *The Sparrow Bush*, rhymes by Elizabeth Coatsworth. Text copyright © 1966 by W. W. Norton & Company, Inc.

SCHOLASTIC BOOK SERVICES, A DIVISION OF SCHOLASTIC MAGAZINES, INC.: Adapted from *Christopher Columbus* by Ann McGovern, © 1962 by Ann McGovern.

CHARLES SCRIBNER'S SONS: Adaptation of *Robbie and the Sled Dog Race* by Sara Machetanz, copyright © 1964 Sara Machetanz.

SILVER BURDETT COMPANY, A DIVISION OF GENERAL LEARNING CORPORATION and DOROTHY LOA MCFADDEN: Adaptation of "A Cargo of Snow" from *Growing Up in Puerto Rico* by Dorothy Loa McFadden, © 1958 by Silver Burdett Company.

SIMON & SCHUSTER, INC.: "The Mine" by Bronwyn Mason, "Dusk" by Eve Recht, and "Winter" by John Constant from *Miracles* edited by Richard Lewis, copyright © 1966 by Richard Lewis.

EVELYN SINGER LITERARY AGENCY AND HARVEY HOUSE, INC.: Adaptation of "Daniel Boone and Chief Blackfish" from *Famous Pioneers* by Franklin Folsom, copyright © 1963, by Franklin Folsom.

THE VIKING PRESS, INC.: "The People" from *Under the Tree* by Elizabeth Madox Roberts, copyright 1922 by B. W. Huebsch, Inc.; renewed 1950 by Ivor S. Roberts. "Old Hiram's Goat" from *The Crocodile's Mouth* by Adrien Stoutenburg, copyright © 1966 by Adrien Stoutenburg. All Rights Reserved.

FRANKLIN WATTS, INC.: "A Brave Explorer" adapted from *The First Book of Negroes* by Langston Hughes, copyright 1952 by Franklin Watts, Inc.

Illustrations on pages 285, 286 and 289 are reproduced from THE HARCOURT BRACE SCHOOL DICTIONARY copyright © 1968 by Harcourt Brace Jovanovich, Inc.

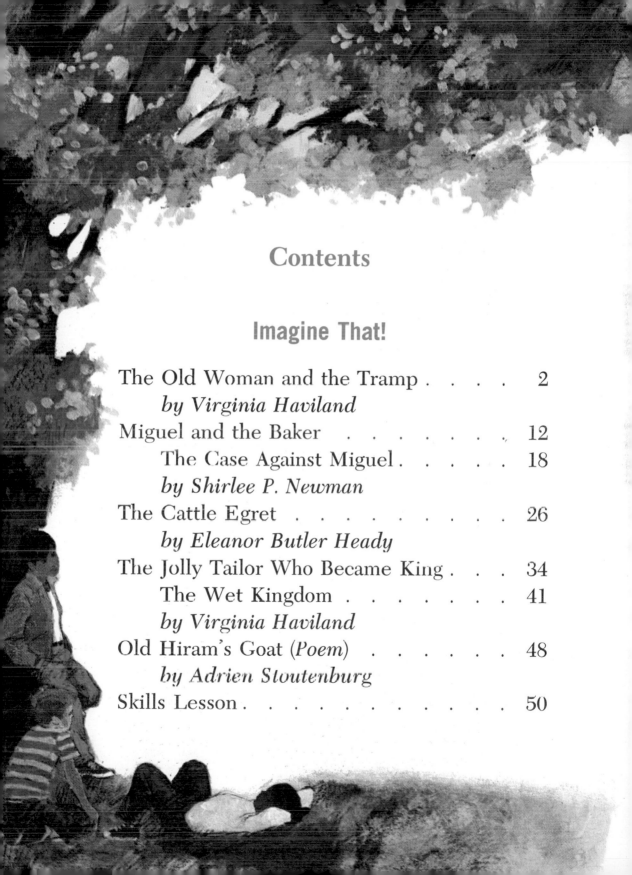

Contents

Imagine That!

Follow the Sun

America's Yesterdays

Friends Along the Way

Today and Tomorrow

The Horse Who Had His Picture in the Paper
by Phyllis McGinley

PICTURE ACKNOWLEDGMENTS: Photographs are from the sources listed below:

Page 1, Harbrace; 55, Fred Lyon, Rapho Guillumette; 68–75, Ronald Rose; 87, Chester Dale Collection, National Gallery of Art, Washington, D.C.; 88, West Baffin Eskimo Cooperative; 89, Jose Verde Orive, Institute of Fine Arts, Mexico; 90, The Brooklyn Museum; 91, The Tate Gallery; 92, The Brooklyn Museum; 99, Ewing Galloway; 149, Bruce Roberts, Rapho Guillumette; 201, Harbrace; 203, General Electric; 204, Harbrace, Courtesy of Bohacks; 206, IBM; 208, Harbrace; 214, General Motors; 216, Aeroglide Systems; 218, Bell Aerosystems; 219, British Railways; 220, U.S. Navy; 223, AT&T; 228–29, NASA; 231, General Dynamics; 233, Stan Wayman, Life Magazine © Time Inc.; 234–5, Scripps Institute of Oceanography; 236, U.S. Navy; 239, Stan Wayman, Life Magazine © Time Inc.; 246, Harbrace; 247, Chris Reeberg, DPI; 248, Sikorsky Aircraft; 249, Harbrace, Courtesy of Bloomingdales, New York; 250, Fred Lyon, Rapho Guillumette.

The artists in this book and the pages on which their work appears are as follows: Raymond Ameijide, pp. 12–25; Dave Blossom, pp. 56–66; Ward Brackett, pp. 135–143, 159–171; Arthur Chitouras, pp. 2–10; John Daly, pp. 211, 242–243; Matt Delfino, Jr. pp. 186–194; Diamond Art Studio, pp. 284, 287–288, 290–292; Graphic 70, p. 120, George Guzzi, pp. 34–47, 50–53, 97, 144, 146, 183–185, 196–199, 252–256; Harbrace Illustrations, pp. 94, 225–226; Jack Hern, pp. 26–33, 121–134; John Jones, pp. 114–119; Peter Landa, p. 76; Charles Sovek, pp. 100–113; Ben Stahl, pp. 77–85, 150–158, 172–181; Susan Swan, p. 48.

Ring Around the World

Ring around the world
Taking hands together
All across the temperate
And the torrid weather.
Past the royal palm-trees
By the ocean sand
Make a ring around the world
Taking each other's hand;
In the valleys, on the hill,
Over the prairie spaces,
There's a ring around the world
Made of children's friendly faces.

ANNETTE WYNNE

Imagine That

The Old Woman and the Tramp

A tramp was once making his way through a forest. He had little hope of finding a place to stay before night set in. But all of a sudden, he saw bright lights shining between the trees. He discovered a cottage with a fire burning in the fireplace. How good it would be, he thought, to warm himself before that blaze, and to find a bite of food! So he went over to the cottage.

An old woman came to the door.

"Good evening, and well met!" said the tramp.

"Good evening," said the woman. "And where do you come from?"

"South of the sun, and east of the moon," said the tramp. "And now I am on the way home again, for I have been all over the world."

"You must be a great traveler indeed," said the woman. "What may you be looking for here?"

"Only a place to stay for the night."

"I thought as much," said the woman. "But my cottage is not an inn. Go away at once!"

"My good woman," said the tramp, "you must not be so hard-hearted. People should help one another."

"Help one another?" said the grumpy woman. "Help? Did you ever hear of such a thing? Who will help me, do you think? I haven't a bit of food in the house! No, you must go away."

But the tramp would not give up at the

3

first try. He begged like a starved dog, until at last she gave in and said he could lie on the floor for the night.

"It is better to lie on the floor without sleep than to be cold in the forest deep," he said. He was a merry sort, this tramp, and always ready with a rhyming word.

When he went into the cottage he could see that the woman was not so badly off as she had said she was.

The tramp tried to make himself agreeable as he asked her for something to eat.

"Impossible! Where shall I get it?" asked the woman. "I haven't eaten a drop of food the whole day."

But the tramp was clever, he was.

"Poor old woman, you must be starving. Well, well, I guess I shall have to ask you to have something with me, then."

"Have something with you!" said the woman. "What have you to give, I'd like to know?"

"He who far and wide does roam sees many things not known at home," said the

4

tramp, with more of his rhymes. "Let me
have a pot, old woman!"

The old woman now wondered about this
man. She let him have a big pot.

The tramp filled the pot with water and
put it over the fire. He took a four-inch
nail from his pocket, carefully turned it
around three times in his hand, and dropped
it into the pot.

The woman stared. "What is this going to be?" she asked.

"Nail broth," said the tramp, and began to stir the water with a big spoon.

"Nail broth?" asked the woman.

"Yes, nail broth," said the tramp.

The old woman had seen and heard much in her time, but that anybody could make broth with a nail, well, she had never heard the like of this before.

"That's something for poor people to know," she said, "and I should like to learn how to make it."

If she wanted to learn she had only to

watch him, he said, and went on stirring.

The old woman followed the tramp's hand with her eyes as he stirred the broth.

"This usually makes good broth," he said. "But this time it will very likely be rather thin, for this whole week I have been making broth with the same nail. If only I had a handful of flour to add, that would make it all right. But what one has to go without, it's no use thinking more about," and once again he stirred the broth.

"Well, I think I have a bit of flour somewhere," said the old woman. She went to get it, and it was both good and fine.

The tramp began stirring the flour into the broth and went on stirring and stirring, while the woman sat, staring now at him and then at the pot.

"This broth would be good enough for the finest of folk," the tramp now said, "if only I had a bit of salted beef and a few carrots to add. But what one has to go without, it's no use thinking more about."

The old woman began to think about this,

7

and she remembered she had a few carrots and perhaps there was a bit of beef as well. These she found and gave to the tramp, who went on stirring and stirring.

"This will be grand enough for the best folk in the land," he said at last.

"Well, I never!" said the woman. "And just think—all that with a nail!"

"If we had only a little cabbage, we could ask the King himself to have some of this. In fact, this is what he has every evening. That I know, for I have been the King's cook," he said.

"Dear me! Ask the King to have some! Well, I never!" said the woman. She was quite overcome that the tramp should know the King.

"But what one has to go without, it's no use thinking more about," said the tramp.

And then the woman remembered she had some cabbage, and got it for the tramp.

The tramp went on with his stirring, and the woman with her staring, one minute at him and the next at the pot.

8

Suddenly the tramp took out the nail.

"Now it's ready. But with this kind of broth the King and the Queen always have something to drink, and some bread. And then they always have a cloth on the table when they eat," he added. "But what one has to go without, it's no use thinking more about."

By this time the old woman herself was beginning to feel quite grand, I can tell you. She thought it would be nice to eat just the way the King and Queen did, for once. So

9

she got out a cloth, a bottle and glasses,
butter and bread, smoked beef and turkey,
until at last the table looked as if it were
decked for a feast.

Never in her life had the old woman eaten
such a grand feast, and never had she had
such broth. Just think of it, made only with
a nail! She felt so merry at having learned
such a cheap way of making broth that she
could not do enough for the tramp.

The old woman and the tramp then ate
and drank, and drank and ate, until they
couldn't move.

The tramp was ready to lie down on the floor to sleep. But that would never do, thought the old woman. No, that was impossible. Someone so grand must have a bed to lie in.

The tramp did not need to be begged. "Happy are they who meet such good people," he said as he lay on the bed and went to sleep.

Next morning when the tramp woke up, the old woman was ready with breakfast for him. In fact, as he was leaving, she gave him a bright coin.

"And thanks, many thanks, for what you have shown me," she said. "Now that I have learned how to make broth with a nail, I shall live in comfort."

"Well, it isn't very hard, if one only has something good to add to it," said the tramp as he went on his way.

The woman stood at the door staring after him. "Such people don't grow on every tree," she said.

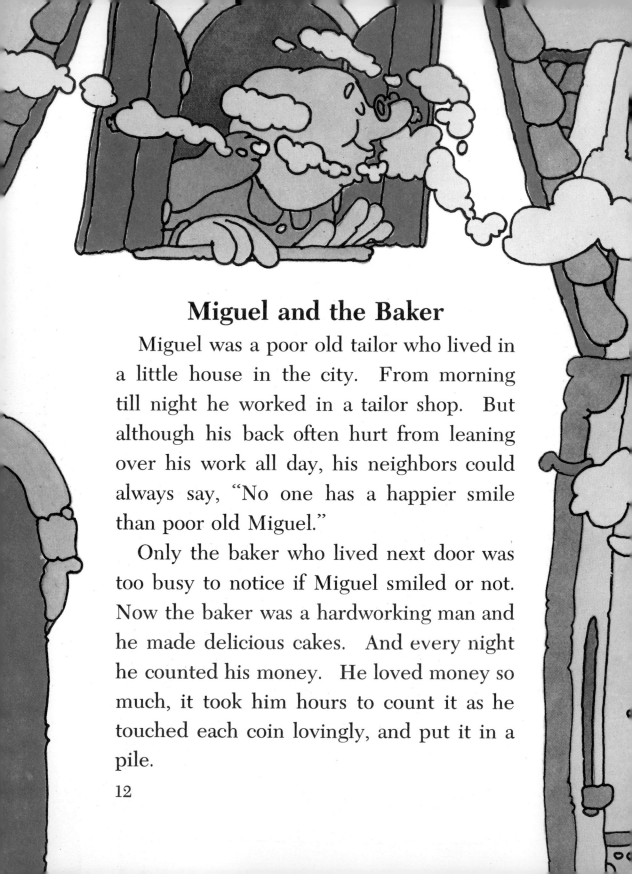

Miguel and the Baker

Miguel was a poor old tailor who lived in a little house in the city. From morning till night he worked in a tailor shop. But although his back often hurt from leaning over his work all day, his neighbors could always say, "No one has a happier smile than poor old Miguel."

Only the baker who lived next door was too busy to notice if Miguel smiled or not. Now the baker was a hardworking man and he made delicious cakes. And every night he counted his money. He loved money so much, it took him hours to count it as he touched each coin lovingly, and put it in a pile.

12

Although the baker hardly ever spoke to him, Miguel felt himself lucky to live next door to the bake shop. When he got up in the morning, Miguel would open his window wide. He would enjoy the delicious smells of freshly baked bread and cake.

One morning while Miguel was sniffing as usual, the baker stepped outside his shop for a breath of air. Looking up, he saw Miguel at his window. The baker's face grew red and angry. "What right does Miguel have to enjoy the smells of my baking for free?" he thought. "Miguel!" he called out. "It's time you paid me for smelling my bread and cake each morning."

Miguel laughed. "You make a joke,
Baker! Ha ha! I didn't know you could be
so funny!" And Miguel leaned out the
window and sniffed some more.

"A joke?" the baker roared. "I make no
joke! I work all night at my ovens. I use
the finest flour, the fattest raisins, the
sweetest nuts. Why should you enjoy them
and pay me nothing for your enjoyment?"

"Why, he is serious," Miguel thought.
"How funny! He seriously thinks I should
pay him for the smells that come from his
shop!"

14

Miguel could not help himself. He started to laugh. He laughed and laughed and laughed! He roared and rolled on the floor! He held his sides and laughed some more!

One by one, the other neighbors leaned out the window. "What's going on?" the man up the street said. "What's so funny?"

"The baker—he—he thinks I should pay him for smelling his bread and cakes!" Miguel could hardly talk for laughing so hard.

The man up the street joined him in laughter. So did the woman across the way and the boy at the corner. In seconds, all of the neighbors were laughing. Everyone, of course, but the baker.

"I'll fix you!" he shouted, shaking his fists so hard his baker's hat shook back and forth on his head. He turned around, went into his shop, and banged the door shut.

Miguel and his neighbors laughed harder than ever.

That afternoon the baker went out to buy flour. As he crossed the road, a little girl came running after him. She sniffed at his coat. Then she said, laughing, "How much do I owe you for that sniff, Baker?"

A group of boys joined in the fun. Following the baker around the corner, they laughed and teased. Now the baker was angrier than ever! "Everyone is making fun of me! There's just one thing to do. I'll go to the courthouse and see the judge."

The judge listened to the baker's story quietly. Not once did he laugh, or even smile.

"—so, Judge," the baker finished, "Miguel has enjoyed the smells of my baking for years. And never has he paid me so much as one silver coin."

"Hmm," the judge said, "I see what you mean. I shall go over the case carefully and decide fairly."

The baker thanked the judge and went home.

The Case Against Miguel

Three days later, a court notice was posted in town.

"THE CASE OF BAKER AGAINST MIGUEL," the notice read.

"BOTH MUST APPEAR BEFORE THE JUDGE TOMORROW. MIGUEL MUST BRING TO COURT A HUNDRED SILVER COINS."

"What shall I do?" Miguel thought, when he saw the notice. "I don't have fifty silver coins, let alone a hundred!"

But the next morning the man from down the street appeared at Miguel's door. He handed Miguel a bag of coins.

"Thank you, dear neighbor," said Miguel, "but if I lose the case, how will I ever repay you?"

The man said, "The coins are yours. All the neighbors joined together to give you these. Don't worry about paying them back."

But Miguel did worry. He thought, "If I lose the case, I will repay all I owe them if it takes a lifetime!"

That afternoon the courtroom was filled with wondering, whispering people. The judge's booming voice quieted everyone down. "Baker," he said, "rise and tell your side of the case."

The baker got to his feet. Not taking his eyes off the bag of money in Miguel's hands, he spoke. "All my life I have worked hard, Judge," he said. "I bake the finest of breads, the lightest of cakes. The flour is the smoothest, the raisins the fattest, the nuts the sweetest. And every morning Miguel opens his window and sniffs at the delicious smells from my ovens.

"Is this fair?" the baker went on. "I ask you, Judge. Is it fair that I work so hard before a hot oven while my neighbor Miguel sits at his window and enjoys the delicious smells—free?"

The judge looked serious.

The baker shook his head. "No," he said, "it is not fair. I should have payment."

The judge listened to every word, then he said, "How much do you think you should be paid, Baker?"

The baker smiled. "Well, Judge," he said, "because of the cost of the good things I use, I think a hundred silver coins would be about right." The baker sat down.

The judge turned to Miguel. "Rise, Miguel," he said.

His legs shaking, Miguel rose.

"Is what you have just heard true?"

asked the judge. "Does the smell of freshly baked bread and cake come to your window every day?"

"Yes, Judge. That's true."

"And are the smells good smells or bad smells?" asked the judge. "Are they an enjoyment or a bother?"

"Enjoyment," Miguel said.

The judge rapped on his table. "Then hand the bag of coins to the baker," he said.

The courtroom was quiet as Miguel did so. The baker grabbed the money bag. Turning to leave, he said, "Thank you, Judge!"

"Ah, just one minute, Baker. Let's make sure there's no money missing," said the judge. "Empty the bag and count the money."

The baker untied the bag and emptied the money onto the table. How those silver coins glowed in the sunlight! How prettily they rang as they bounced about!

One by one, the baker touched the shiny

silver. Then he returned the coins to the bag. "There are a hundred, Judge," he said. "Thank you for your wise judgment!" He started to leave.

"Ah, just one minute, Baker," said the judge. "Give the bag of money back to Miguel."

Miguel stared in surprise. So did the baker. So did everyone else.

The judge rose. "In the name of the people of this city," he said, "I shall now give my judgment in the case of Baker against Miguel."

Everyone sat on the edge of his chair.

"You, Miguel," said the judge, "have enjoyed the smell of the baker's goods. You, Baker, have enjoyed the feel of Miguel's money. The case is closed."

The courtroom was still. A minute passed. Then another. Suddenly someone in the back of the room started to laugh. Someone else joined in. Now the courtroom rocked with laughter!

"Hurrah for Miguel!"

As he listened to the laughter, the meaning of the judge's words became clear to Miguel. He had won! He owed the baker nothing for his smells! Smiling, Miguel handed the money bag to the man who lived down the street. "Now I owe no one!" he cried.

"Yes!" his neighbors agreed. "And you can sniff the baker's goods as much as you want!" Lifting Miguel to their shoulders, the people marched out of the courthouse.

The courtroom was quiet now. The judge sat back in his chair. He looked serious. Then all at once his face broke into smiles. He started to laugh. He laughed and laughed and laughed. He roared and rolled on the floor. He held his sides and laughed some more! "Tomorrow morning, I shall visit Miguel," he thought. "I'd like to enjoy these delicious smells, too!"

The Cattle Egret

It was evening again, time to hear a story from Grandmother. The children were gathered in a circle, their grandmother in the middle. Nupe, the cattle egret, eyed them from the top of the thorn bush fence which protected the cattle and goats from lions during the night. He flew away to perch on the back of a brown and white cow.

"Tell   us   a   story   about   Nupe,

26

Grandmother," urged one of the boys. "Do you know a story about him?"

"Yes indeed," laughed Grandmother. And this is the story she told.

Nupe, the cattle egret, lives in the fields with the cattle. He follows them wherever they go, sometimes sitting on their backs for a better look at the world.

But Nupe did not *always* live with the cattle. This is how it began.

There had been no rain for many months.

The rivers stopped running. The springs were dry. Plants blackened and died in the sun. Stores of grain and roots were gone. People and animals could find nothing to eat or drink.

When Kanda, the chief, saw the unhappiness in his country, he called a meeting of all the people, animals, birds, and insects.

"We must find water," said the chief. "If there is anyone who can find water, I will make him chief of his kind, if he be

man, bird, animal, or insect." When
the chief had finished talking, there was
not a sound.

Then shyly, from his perch on a thorn
bush, Nupe, the egret, spoke. "I will try
to get water. I can lose nothing by trying."

A cheer went up from the dry throats of
all who were gathered there. "Nupe,
Nupe, good luck to you, Nupe."

"Please look for water now," urged Kanda, the chief. "We can't wait much longer."

"Very well," said Nupe and flew to the dry bed of a river where he began to dig with his beak, saying, "I will peck, peck, peck until water comes."

He pecked around and around, making a deep hole. All the birds, animals, insects, and people came to watch and cheer him on. Finally, the egret brought up mud on his beak. The watchers gathered closer, whispering in excitement.

"Please don't crowd," said Nupe, as he stopped to rest. "I'll need a lot of room and fresh air if I am to dig to clear water. I'll peck, peck, peck until I have found water for everyone, but you must be patient with me. My beak is small and water is far down in the earth."

Everyone moved away to give the egret room to work. All day he pecked until he had a very deep hole and was so far down that no one could see him.

Kanda, the chief, looked over the side of the hole. "Water yet, Nupe?"

"There should be much water soon, for it is wet here now."

At that minute a clear stream of water rushed forth, rising into the air and soaking Nupe. He flew up from the hole while

30

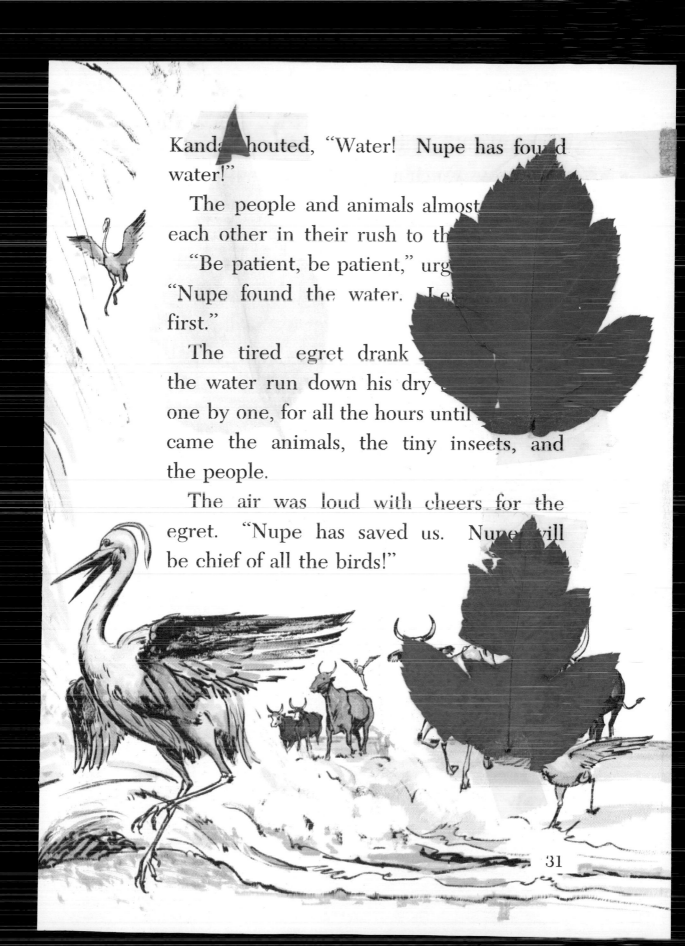

Kanda shouted, "Water! Nupe has found water!"

The people and animals almost [...] each other in their rush to th[...]

"Be patient, be patient," urg[...] "Nupe found the water. Le[...] first."

The tired egret drank [...] the water run down his dry [...] one by one, for all the hours until [...] came the animals, the tiny insects, and the people.

The air was loud with cheers for the egret. "Nupe has saved us. Nupe will be chief of all the birds!"

While all this was happening, Nupe sat on a tree watching and thinking. "Chief of the birds? Why would I want to be chief of the birds? I'd rather have a free life."

When all had finished drinking, Chief Kanda gathered them together again.

"Now we must give Nupe his reward. Come, friend, so that I may make you chief of the birds."

"But I'd rather not be chief," said the egret. "Give me some other reward, something less likely to make trouble."

"Not be chief?" said Kanda. "I can't understand that."

"I like a free and quiet life," said Nupe. "A chief cannot have that."

"True. What would you like?"

"Only some cattle for my own," said Nupe.

"Cattle? Is that all?"

"Yes, Chief Kanda. Cattle are such lovely, quiet beasts."

"He can have all my cattle if he wishes," shouted a voice from the crowd. Others called out, "Yes, yes, all our cattle."

"You may choose any cattle in the land because you have found the water," said the chief. "You may live with them in peace. You and your children will guard the cattle."

"Thank you, kind chief," said Nupe, and he flew away and perched on the back of a spotted cow.

To this day, the egrets live in the fields with the cattle, playing and feeding beside them or sitting on their backs in the sunshine.

The Jolly Tailor Who Became King

Once upon a time, in a small town, there lived a jolly young tailor named Mr. Nitechka. He was a very thin man. All tailors are thin as a needle and thread, but Mr. Nitechka was the thinnest of all. He could have gone through the eye of his own needle. But for all this, he was a very happy young man, and a handsome one, too.

Now Mr. Nitechka would have lived very happily in the little town had it not been for a teller of fortunes who happened to be in the town. This is the fortune she read from Nitechka's hand:

"If you leave this town and walk always westward, you will reach a place where you will be made King."

34

Nitechka laughed at this. But that very night he dreamed that he indeed became a King, and that from great riches he grew so fat that he was huge. Upon waking he thought, "Maybe it is true—who knows? Get up, Mr. Nitechka, and go westward."

He took a bundle with a hundred needles and a thousand miles of thread and his other tailoring tools, and started westward. But he had not gone far when a little wind blew across a field. And because Nitechka was so very thin, the wind was just strong enough to carry him off.

The jolly tailor flew through the air, laughing all the while at such a ride. Soon, however, the wind became tired and let him down to earth. His head was spinning and he did not know where he was until someone shouted, "What's this?"

35

Mr. Nitechka look around and saw that he was in a wheat field and that the wind had thrown him right into the arms of a scarecrow. The scarecrow was very well dressed for a scarecrow. His clothes were those of a gentleman. They were only a little bit worn. He had two sticks for feet and also sticks for hands.

Nitechka took off his little cap, bowed very low, and said in his thin voice, "I'm very sorry if I stepped on your foot. I'm Mr. Nitechka, the tailor."

36

"I'm pleased to meet you," answered the scarecrow, bowing as well as he could. "I am Count Scarecrow, and my coat of arms is four sticks. I watch the sparrows here so that they won't eat the wheat. I am very brave and would like to fight only with wild animals, like lions. However, they don't often come to eat the wheat. Where are you going, Sir?"

Nitechka bowed again, knowing that gentlemen did this often. "Where do I go, Mr. Count?" he said. "I'm going

westward to a place where I will become King."

"Is it possible?" asked the Count.

"Of course!" said the tailor, "I was born to be a king. And perhaps you, Mr. Count, would like to go with me. It will be jollier, and maybe you'll make your fortune, too."

"All right," answered the scarecrow. "I'm already tired of being here. But please, Mr. Nitechka, sew up the tears in my clothes a bit. I might like to marry someone on the way, and so I should be neat and handsome."

"Gladly!" said Nitechka. He went to work, and in an hour the scarecrow's

clothes were almost like new. The sparrows in the field laughed at him a little, but he paid them no mind as he walked proudly beside Mr. Nitechka.

On the way, the two became great friends. They usually slept in a wheat field. Nitechka tied himself to the scarecrow with a piece of thread so that the wind could not carry the tailor off again. And when dogs fell upon them, the scarecrow, who was very brave, pulled out his foot and threw it after them. Then he tied it again to his body.

They went on their way toward a town they had heard of, where the old king had just died. As they drew near to it, they were greatly puzzled to see that all around the town it was sunshiny and warm. But right over the town, the rain poured from the sky as from a bucket.

"If I go in there," the scarecrow said, "my hat will get wet."

"And even I don't want to become king of such a wet kingdom," said the tailor.

The Wet Kingdom

Just then some people standing by the gates of the town saw them and rushed toward them. "Please, Gentlemen," called the townspeople, "maybe you can help us."

"And what has happened to you?" asked Nitechka.

"Our King died a week ago, and ever since then, a terrible rain has come down upon our town. We can't even cook, because so much water runs into our fireplaces. We will die!"

"It is too bad," said Nitechka very wisely.

"Oh, very bad!" said the townspeople. "And we are most sorry for the King's daughter. The poor thing can't stop crying, and this brings even more water."

"That *is* bad," said Nitechka, still more wisely.

"Help us, help us!" urged the people. "Do you know what the Princess promises as a reward to the man who stops the rain? She will marry him, and then he will become King."

41

"Truly?" cried Nitechka. "Count Scarecrow, let's go to the town. We should try to help them."

Through the terrible rain they went, to the Princess. Upon seeing Nitechka, she cried out, "Oh, what a handsome young man!"

He bowed and said, "Is it true, Princess, that you will marry the one who stops the rain? And he will become a King?"

"So I promised," said the Princess.

"Very well," answered the tailor. "*I* am going to stop the rain."

42

So saying, he nodded to Count Scarecrow
and they left the Princess.

For three days the scarecrow and the
tailor thought and thought and thought of
ways to stop the rain. And all the while the
rain fell and fell and fell. Suddenly Nitechka
gave a cry of joy.

"I know where the rain comes from!" he
said.

"Where from?" asked the scarecrow.

"From the sky!" said the tailor.

"Eh!" said the scarecrow impatiently. "I
know that too!"

"Yes," said Nitechka, "but why does it always fall over the town only, and never elsewhere?"

"Because elsewhere there is nice weather," said Count Scarecrow.

"But tell me," said the tailor patiently, "how *long* has it rained?"

"They say since the King died," said the Count.

"You see!" shouted Nitechka. "Now I know everything. The King was so great and mighty that when he died and went to heaven he made a huge hole in the sky."

"Oh, true, true!" said the Count.

"The rain poured through the hole," said Nitechka, "and it will pour until the end of the world if the hole isn't sewed up."

Count Scarecrow looked at him in wonder. "In all my life, I have never seen such a wise tailor," said he.

Nitechka told the townspeople to bring all the ladders in the town, tie them together, and lean them against the sky. He took his hundred needles and, threading one, went up the ladders. Count Scarecrow stayed at the bottom to unwind the thousand miles of thread.

45

When Nitechka got to the very top, he saw there was a huge hole in the sky, a hole just as big as the town. A piece of the sky was hanging down, and through this hole the water poured.

So he went to work and sewed and sewed for two days. His fingers grew stiff and he became very tired, but he did not stop. When he had finished sewing, he ironed out the sky and then, tired out, went down the ladders.

46

Once more there was sunshine over the town. Count Scarecrow almost went mad with joy, as did all the townspeople. The Princess wiped her eyes that were almost cried out. Throwing herself on Nitechka's neck, she kissed him lovingly.

"Long live King Nitechka!" cheered the townspeople. "Long live the King!"

So the jolly little tailor married the Princess and was King for a long time. The rain never again fell in his kingdom. He grew fatter and jollier. And in his good fortune, Nitechka did not forget his old friend, Count Scarecrow. He made him the gardener of the Kingdom, to drive away the sparrows from the King's head.

Old Hiram's Goat

Old Hiram's goat was feeling fine,
ate three red shirts right off the line.
His master grabbed him by the back
and tied him to the railroad track.

The goat just wagged his runty tail
and started nibbling at a rail;
next thing, he chewed a railroad tie,
and finished off with cinder pie.

He started over, on a thistle,
and never heard the distant whistle;
a train was roaring down the draw.
Old Hiram's wife both heard and saw.

She screamed and ran out of the house.
"Hiram!" she hollered at her spouse.
"If that goat dies" — she wrung her hands —
"what will we do with our tin cans?"

Old Hiram ran but wrenched his knee.
"Oh, what a fool I was," groaned he.
He cupped his hand about his ear
and yelled to warn the engineer.

Just then the train slammed into sight.
The goat looked up and shook with fright.
He heaved a sigh, as if in pain,
coughed up those shirts, and flagged the
    train.

That goat was clever, people say,
to use those red shirts in that way.
As for me, there's one big question:
Was it brains — or indigestion?

ADRIEN STOUTENBURG

Vowel Sounds and Letters

You know that every word must have a vowel sound and at least one vowel letter: a, e, i, o, u, y. You know, too, that each vowel letter can stand for more than one sound. Think of the different sounds of *a* in the following words: *taxes, brace, salt, apart, water.*

There are pairs of vowels that stand for one vowel sound. Think of f*au*cets, tr*ay*, r*ai*n, w*ei*gh, cr*ie*d, s*oi*l.

Sometimes one pair of vowel letters stands for more than one sound. Think of *bread* and *great, boom* and *hook, crowd* and *known, count* and *young, sour* and *pour.*

There are 19 different vowel sounds, but there are more than 120 different ways to spell these 19 sounds.

How do we ever learn to read English? Well, for one thing, we learn sounds and letters gradually, or a few at a time.

Gradually, we learn all the ways that letters can be combined to stand for the sounds we know. Then we can read almost any word we meet.

Gradually you have learned what vowel sounds to try when you meet new words. If you came to this word—*braid*—you would not try "brood" or "breed" or "browd." You would remember that *ai* usually stands for the vowel sound you hear in *rain*.

Now read this sentence:

Linda has a new plaid skirt.

Did you read *plaid* as if it sounded like *played*? If you did, you probably said to yourself, "That doesn't sound like any skirt I ever heard of. But I have heard of a /plad/ skirt." Then you might look in the dictionary to see if you were right.

How Many Sounds for O?

The letter *o* is very useful. It can stand for the five different vowel sounds you hear in these words—*clock, ocean, cork, wolf, women.* But in most syllables, *o*

51

stands for the sound you hear in *hot*. Try that sound first, when you meet a new word with *o*. In many words *o* stands for the sound you hear in *most*. Try that sound next. If *o* is followed by *r*, try the sound you hear in *cork* and *born*.

What sound does *o* stand for in these words? *month, tons, cover, front, stomach, shovel, nothing*.

The letter *o* is often combined with another vowel. In one-syllable words that end in *e*, the *o* sound is often long. Think of *hole, rope, stove, broke*. But the pattern *o-e* stands for other sounds, too. Think of *move, done, come, gone*.

When *o* and *a* are combined, they often stand for the vowel sound in *road*. When *o* and *i* are combined, they usually stand for the vowel sound in *coin*. What sound do you hear when *o* and *y* are combined, as in *enjoy* and *toy*?

When *o* and *u* are combined, they can stand for the different sounds you hear in these words — *mouse, shoulder, rough, could, group.* When you come to a new word with *ou* in it, you may need to look it up in a dictionary.

You know that *w* after a vowel usually stands for one vowel sound. Do you hear the same vowel sound in *snow* and *crowd*?

Try This

All the words in each group below have the same vowel sound. Can you think of another word that belongs in each group? The word must have the same vowel letters and the same vowel sound.

chooses	window	pound	young
shoot	owe	rouse	rough
tool	bowl	south	touch

The Schwa Sound

In words of more than one syllable, the sound of the vowel is weak in syllables that are not accented. Say these words to yourself—*problem, canyon, foreman, pencil, walrus.* You can hear a different vowel sound in the first syllable of each of these words. But the vowel sound in the second syllable in every word sounds the same, although each vowel letter is different. We call this weak vowel sound a *schwa*. In dictionaries, the sign for a schwa looks like this — ə.

Try This

Tell which vowel in each of these words stands for the schwa sound. Tell which syllable in each word is accented.

kingdom	alarm	finger	gentle
tunnel	awake	otter	simple
metal	apart	shoulder	heaven
captain	around	thunder	little

What Did You Learn?

1. Is there any word that does not have a vowel sound?
2. Does every syllable have a vowel sound?
3. Make a list of words with *o* in them to show all the different sounds *o* can stand for. You may combine *o* with other vowels, too.

Follow the Sun

Robbie and the Sled Dog Race

One morning Robbie March climbed down out of bed so early that the fire hadn't been lit yet. Robbie made the fire, got dressed, and went out.

First he went to the post where Nubbin was chained. He set a pan of fish soup down in front of the dog. Then he carried pans to Flip and Flop.

The sled dogs did not move toward the food. Only their tails moved, brushing out nests in the snow behind them.

"All right," Robbie said, and three black noses dived into three pans.

56

The fish soup was made from fish Robbie had helped his father catch in the summer. Robbie hoped it would make his dogs run fast. Today was the final "three dogger" race at the Alaska Snow Fair. And Mark Wood's time was two minutes and ten seconds better than Robbie's. Still, he was sure his team wouldn't disappoint him.

Robbie went over to Nubbin and rubbed the soft fur behind her ears. Then he looked closely at her paws to see if there were any cuts. They were fine. He checked Flip's and Flop's paws. They were fine too.

As Robbie checked over his dogs he thought about the months he had worked to make them a team. He remembered the first times they had been put in harness — Nubbin beside a leader. That was the way they had learned to go right when he called "gee" and to turn left at the word "haw."

Robbie wanted a well-trained team, so he had worked hard to teach them to mind. And they had grown stronger with runs of over a mile to the mailbox every day.

"You must be trying to make up that time right now, Son," his father said from the doorway.

"Just woke up and wanted to get up," Robbie answered, grinning. Really, he hadn't been able to sleep because he was so excited.

The dogs were excited too. When Robbie and Mr. March went out for them after breakfast the three dogs barked and ran around in circles and dug at the ground.

During the drive to the Snow Fair, the dogs quieted down, curled themselves up and went to sleep. But when Mr. March parked in the field beside the track, they woke up. Other teams were barking and the dogs grew more excited than ever. They jerked against their chains and barked back.

As they put the harnesses on the dogs, Mr. March said, "The dogs do seem to be in good shape. But Mark's dogs *are* larger."

"I know," Robbie said, "but that doesn't mean they're better. My team's better trained."

"That's true, Son. I just don't want you to be too disappointed if you lose," said Mr. March.

When the dogs were in harness, Mr. March and Robbie took the dogs to their place behind Mark Wood's team. Mark's dogs were excited too and Mark and his keeper could barely hold them while the timer counted off the seconds. At the count of "one" Mark's team was off.

After a two minute wait, it would be time for Robbie's team to go. Mr. March looked back at Robbie. "Just catch up to Mark, Son, and you've made up two minutes. Then you've only ten seconds to go. Good luck!"

The timer began the countdown. "One minute, thirty seconds . . . fifteen seconds . . . five, four, three, two, one!"

"Let's go," Robbie shouted. Nubbin and the team shot forward.

The Race

Robbie started out running behind the sled. When he was out of breath, he jumped on the runners. Then he stood on one foot and pushed with the other. As soon as he caught his breath, he jumped off to run again.

Uphill, downhill, and across roads that were blocked off to traffic, Robbie ran and drove his team. But Robbie was worried. He was pushing his team more than he ever had, and still he had not caught up with Mark.

61

"Run, Nubbin, run, run, run," he urged.
Up the steepest hill Robbie pushed until
he was panting as hard as the dogs. And
then, just over the top, he saw something
that made him hold onto his sled and breathe
harder than ever.

At the foot of the hill were Mark and
his team. But instead of running straight
ahead, they were turning left into the
woods. Robbie could hear the dogs barking
and Mark yelling. He saw Mark jump off
the sled, turn it over and run to his leader.
Then Robbie saw why the dogs had turned

off-trail. At the edge of the woods stood
a huge moose.

Nubbin, Flip, and Flop caught sight
of the dogs and the moose at the same
moment Robbie did. All at once and all
together they shot forward, flying down
the hill. Flip and Flop began to bark
wildly and Nubbin's ears and tail went
straight up. At the place where Mark's
dogs had turned off, Nubbin began to go
left too.

"Gee, Nubbin," Robbie yelled. "Gee!"

Hearing Robbie's voice, Nubbin jerked back on-trail again. Not Flip and Flop. They pulled toward the moose with all their might. Robbie knew they could pull Nubbin along with them.

"Gee, Flip. Gee, Flop," he shouted.

Flip stopped for a moment.

"Gee," Robbie shouted. "Gee, gee, gee."

At that, Flip pulled back in line and Flop, feeling the jerk on the harness, followed.

As Robbie passed Mark's team, he looked back. Mark was having trouble. His dogs seemed to be tangled in their harnesses.

"Here's my chance to get ahead," Robbie thought. "Let's go, Nubbin," he sang out.

Then he had another thought. The moose might be upset enough by the dogs to go after Mark.

Robbie knew he had to send help back to Mark. He must, even if it meant losing seconds — even if it meant losing the race.

Beside the trail, Robbie saw four men watching the race.

"Whoa," he called to Nubbin. "Whoa!"

Nubbin turned her head. "Stop," she seemed to ask, "when the finish line is ahead?"

"Whoa," Robbie called again. Then he said to the men, "Mark Wood's team went after a moose and got tangled up."

"We'd better go help him," one man said, starting to hurry down the trail.

"Wait," another shouted after him. "Here comes Mark now." He turned towards Robbie. "Get going, boy."

But Robbie was already going.

"Run, Nubbin, run," Robbie shouted. He jumped off the sled and ran until he could run no longer. When he jumped on again, he turned for a quick look. Mark was getting closer!

"Faster, Nubbin, faster," Robbie cried. He didn't look back again but he knew Mark was close. He could hear him calling to his team. Any moment he expected Mark to call "trail" and he would have to pull over.

Up ahead Robbie saw the crowd at the finish line. They were yelling and clapping.

Then he heard the timer's voice booming over the loudspeaker. "Here they come now. It's Robin March and Mark Wood. The teams are very close. Robin March is in the lead. Now Robin is crossing the

66

finish line. This will be a close one. . . .
Mark Wood is coming up fast. . . . Mark is
over. . . ."

Robbie stopped his sled and leaned
against it trying to catch his breath. He
had crossed first but had he made up the
time needed to beat Mark? The timer
didn't say. He was calling off the other
teams.

Nubbin was panting so hard she shook.
Robbie went to her, dropped to his knees
and put his arm around her.

"You are the best leader in all of
Alaska," he told her. "And you are the
best team," he said to Flip and Flop,
"even if we lose." He tried not to sound
disappointed.

"Son!" Robbie heard his father's excited
voice. "Son, you won. You won by just
two seconds." Mr. March patted Robbie's
shoulder. "The best trained team turned
out to be the best team after all, didn't it?"

Robbie felt good all over. "Sure *did*,"
he agreed, for that was something he'd
believed since his first "gee" and "haw."

Inoke Sails the South Seas

In the tropical South Seas there are many islands. One of the most beautiful groups is called Fiji. There are more than three hundred islands in Fiji. On one of these lives a boy called Inoke.

Like most boys and girls, Inoke goes to school. More than anything, he wants to become a man of the sea and work on one of the small sailing boats carrying copra, bananas, and people around the islands.

68

Inoke lives with his family in a house made from coconut trees. Everything is tied together, and no nails are used. The house is cool in the hot weather and keeps out the heavy tropical rains.

One day Inoke hears that he is wanted to help unload Mesake's boat.

Inoke is excited. Many times he has hoped that Mesake would ask him to help with his boat, but he has been too small. Now Mesake needs him to unload the great green hands of bananas and to load bags

of copra.   Perhaps one day he will ask Inoke
to help him sail the boat.

Soon Mesake's boat is loaded and ready
for another trip.   Inoke watches as the boat
moves slowly away.

When Mesake returns from his trip, he brings with him a chief from another island to talk about plans for a new school.

Inoke decides it is time to ask Mesake if he will allow him to sail on his boat one day. To his joy, Mesake says: "Yes, if you do well at school, I will take you for a trial trip."

So Inoke begins to study his school books right away. He works hard at school, and the days seem very long. But he thinks of Mesake and his boat, and he studies even harder.

Then one day his teacher calls him out in front of the class. Inoke's heart beats fast with excitement, for there is a smile on the teacher's face. He tells Inoke that he is pleased with his work. He says that Inoke is now ready to leave school.

Inoke runs to Mesake and tells him the good news. Mesake says that he will keep his promise and that he will take Inoke on a

short trial trip to a nearby island the next
day.

That night Inoke prepares for his trip.
By the light of a hurricane lamp, he gathers

his belongings and ties them in a mat, for
this is the way all Fijians carry their things
when they travel.

Inoke's first job the next day is to help
Mesake bring his boat to the shore for
loading. The passengers pile their goods

74

on board, and soon they are ready to put
out to sea.

Inoke's job is to stand on the bowsprit
and watch for dangerous coral reefs. He
calls out to Mcsake: "All clear ahead, sir."

75

Japanese Poems

Watching the full moon,
a small hungry boy forgets
to eat his supper.

BASHO

Above the ruins
of a shrine, a chestnut tree
still lifts its candles.

BASHO

My horse clip-clopping
over a field . . . oh ho! I'm
part of the picture!

BASHO

Night over the pond
of the temple garden . . . geese
adrift and asleep . . .

SHIKI

TRANSLATED BY HARRY BEHN

A Cargo of Snow

This was a wonderful time of year for Lupe. The holidays were so near that schools in Puerto Rico had already closed for Christmas. Besides, there was something special. There was a cargo of snow from the north that Doña Felísa, lady mayor of San Juan, had promised the boys and girls. There would soon be snow in warm, sunny San Juan!

The morning the snow was to arrive, Lupe's father woke her up early.

"Lupe," he called. "We'll have to hurry if you want to see the cargo of snow arrive!"

"I'm coming, Papi," answered Lupe. Lupe hurried. She knew Papi wouldn't be able to wait for her. Her father worked at International Airport. He was one of the baggage men who helped unload the big planes. Maybe he would even drive one of the baggage trucks that unloaded the cargo of snow from New England.

On the bus to the airport, Lupe was so excited she was sitting on the edge of her seat. Even without the snow, there was nothing she liked better than to visit the airport with her father. She liked to watch the planes unload. Lupe noticed everything. She noticed how the baggage men carefully placed each piece of cargo on the trucks to spread the load evenly. The bags were set closely together, too, to keep them from sliding.

And she liked to walk around the airport building too. She noticed the hotel guests standing outside their rooms, watching the planes landing and taking off. Other people were watching from the visitors' deck. That was Lupe's favorite spot.

It was wonderful to see a great silver plane move up its runway, turn, and roaring, pick up power and speed for a clean

take-off. It was just as exciting to watch a
far-away plane circle the airport and come
down for a landing.

The bus driver's voice woke Lupe up
from her daydreams. "International
Airport!"

Lupe was the first one to hop off. As
they walked through the building to the
field, Papi was close behind her.

"What's your hurry, Lupe?" asked Papi.
"Are you catching a plane to the north?"

"No," laughed Lupe, "but I wish I were.
Someday I will, though, won't I, Papi?"

"I'm sure you will," answered Papi. "But for now, Lupe, remember that you're a guest, not a passenger. Mind you keep out of the way of the baggage trucks—and don't go too near the planes."

"I'll be a good guest," promised Lupe.

As they hurried through the building, Lupe looked around at the shops where people were buying gifts or things to eat. She saw the ticket office where people were buying tickets to places like Spain, New York, or Mexico.

"The airport is exciting, isn't it, Lupe?" said Papi, looking down at his daughter. "Everything about it. The planes, the people from many places coming and going, the cargoes that come here—"

80

"Like the snow from New England," exclaimed Lupe. "Imagine, snow in Puerto Rico!"

"Yes," said Papi. "A fast plane is bringing snow to Puerto Rico."

"But won't the snow melt, even in a fast plane?" asked Lupe.

"No," answered Papi, "because they are keeping it cold on the plane, just as they do when there's a cargo of fresh foods. Of course, the snow won't last long under our hot sun once you children start playing with it."

81

Lupe shook her head in wonder. It seemed so strange. Yesterday, when she and her friends were playing on the grass under the warm sun, a group of children in the north may have been packing snow into cartons.

Papi went off to work. The plane from New England was to arrive any minute. Lupe raced up to the visitors' deck. She was just in time. The big plane was coming in for a landing.

A few minutes later, a boy and girl came down the plane's steps. They were both bundled up in heavy clothes. Each one was carrying something that Lupe recognized only from pictures she had seen. They were skis.

Newspaper men were snapping pictures of the boy and girl as they stood on either side of the Mayor of San Juan.

Lupe could see her father and some other men begin to unload the cartons of snow from the plane onto trucks. When she looked back to the steps, she saw that the boy and girl had put down their skis and were taking off some of their heavy outer clothes. They laughed and talked easily with the Mayor. Lupe thought that they were probably joking about the weather, and she smiled too.

But now she decided that she'd better get going. Some of the trucks were already on the way to the ball park where the snow was to be unloaded. Lupe wanted to be the first one at the ball park.

She hurried off, but when she got to the ball park, it looked as though everybody in Puerto Rico had gotten there before her! The grandstands were filled with grownups and the field was crowded with thousands and thousands of children.

Soon the Mayor of San Juan drove up with the boy and girl from New England. Then a truckload of snow arrived and the fun began!

Lupe and other girls and boys rushed forward to get the ice cream cartons filled with snow. Lupe's carton felt very cold in her hands. She took off the cover and licked some snow. It was as cold as ice cream—but not as sweet.

Then Lupe threw a handful, but so much snow was already flying about that she couldn't see where her first snowball had gone.

Some of the children were throwing snow at each other, at the children from New England, even at Doña Felísa! Some threw snow at their laughing mothers and fathers in the grandstands. The grownups tried to catch it. When they did, they threw it back at their surprised children.

The smaller children rubbed each other's faces with snow, or stood very quietly watching the strange white stuff melt in their hands.

Quickly, Lupe made another snowball. She was just about to throw it, when a big soft snowball landed on her head. It splashed her face and hair, and felt wet and cold through her dress.

"Got you, didn't I!" a boy she recognized shouted over the noise.

"And I'll get you!" laughed Lupe, grabbing him and pushing a big handful of snow down his neck. Wildly they both ran to get more cartons, stepping in a big puddle of melted snow.

Lupe sighed. She hated to have the snow go so fast. But someday she would fly up north, when snow covered all the ground for miles around. She would learn to ski, and coast, and make a snowman. But for now—there was time to make one more ball of this wonderful snow.

The Equatorial Jungle, by Henri Rousseau

Art Around the World

People all over the world have art. Art is an important part of people's lives not only now, but it has been from very early times. People "speak" through their art. An artist tells his thoughts and feelings through his work, sometimes better than he can with words.

The artist shows the people and places and ways of living he is familiar with. The "world" of an artist in China a thousand years ago is different from the world of an artist living in Mexico now. The artist shows something of his world in his art.

This drawing was done by an Eskimo artist. You can tell something about Eskimo life if you look at it carefully. The drawing is simple, with strong lines and shapes. It was made by cutting lines into a stone. The picture was then printed from the stone.

Hunters at the Floe Edge, by Enooky

The Fruit Stall, by Olga Costa

The Fruit Stall was painted by a Mexican artist. How delicious the fruit looks! The rich ripe colors make it look very inviting. Do you have the same kind of fruit where you live?

Royal Portrait of Bom Bosh

Bom Bosh was king of the African country, Bushongo, more than three hundred years ago. Here is his likeness carved in wood. Notice the square shapes of Bom Bosh's headdress and seat, and the rounded shapes of his face and body.

90

Project for a Family Group, **by Henry Moore**

This family group in metal, by an English artist, could be from any part of the world. Notice how each one of the family is touching another. Their arms almost make a circle. What feeling does this give about the family?

Landscape Scroll, by Ch'ien Ku

This scene is a peaceful one. The soft, quiet colors and the trees on all sides of the house give this feeling. The painting is over four hundred years old. Could you have guessed that the scene is in China?

Poems by Children

Dusk

The sunset bloomed
Like sunny balloons
On holiday streets.
The air was soft and silent.
Swept away
Were all ashes
Of a bright summer's day.
The moon
Took his place
At watching the silent,
sleepy world
Slip by at his feet.

EVE RECHT, Age 11, Australia

Winter

Animals are restless
Birds are in flight,
Butterflies are not out.
Leaves; a gray blanket,
Winter lurks near.

Icy fingers grasp the world.
Snow falls; graceful,
  beautiful, undisturbed.
Silence creeps about.

JOHN CONSTANT, Age 10, Canada

The Mine

Here we are: in the darkness,
Close to the very heart of
  Mother Earth,
Where her blood flows in
  seams of shining coal,
And our picks beat a rhythm
  to her heart,
Where her warm brown flesh
  encloses us
And her rocky bones trap us.

BRONWYN MASON, Age 12, New Zealand

Word Families

In the English language, many words have families. The words in one family are related in meaning. That is because they all have the same root.

A root may be a whole word that you know. *Sleep* is a root in *sleepy* and *sleepiness*. Can you add another word to the "sleep family"? Did you think of *sleepily*? Did you think of *sleepless*?

Many long words are made up of a root to which something has been added at the end or at the beginning.

A part that is added to the end of a word is called a *suffix*. You are familiar with the endings *-s*, *-es*, *-ed*, *-ing*. These endings are *suffixes*. You know other suffixes, too.

Suffixes change the meaning of the *root word*. If you add *-ish* to *fool*, what does *foolish* mean? You know the word *green*. What does *greenish* mean?

change

changing

unchanged changeable changeless changed

Sometimes a suffix adds another syllable to the root word. Say *change*. Now say *changes*. Do you hear two syllables in *changes*? Say *attacked*. Did the suffix *-ed* add another syllable to *attack*?

Knowing root words and suffixes can help you to recognize many new words. Since you know *change*, you can easily recognize *changing, changeless, changeable.* You know the meanings of these words in the *change* "family," too.

Some suffixes are like real words. The suffix *-ful* is like the word *full*. It means "full of" when added to the word *care*. A *careful* person is "full of care." What kind of person is *thoughtful*?

Another suffix that is like a real word is *-able*. You know what *able* means in this sentence: "Bill was *able* to trade his truck for an airplane." When *-able* is added to a word, it adds to the meaning of the root word. An *enjoyable* story is one that can be enjoyed. What does "changeable weather" mean?

Try This

Read the following words. Find the root in each one. Think of how the suffix adds meaning to the root word. Be ready to use each word in a sentence.

1. moveable   4. comfortable
2. beautiful   5. shameful
3. helpful   6. breakable

Probably you noticed that the spelling of a root word is sometimes changed when a suffix is added. Were you able to find *beauty* in *beautiful*?

Two More Suffixes

You are familiar with the suffix *-ness*. You know the words *kindness, gentleness, quietness*. If a girl is *shy*, we speak of her *shyness*. If a piece of wood is *rough*, we speak of its *roughness*. The suffix *-ness* can be added to many words.

The ending *-ment* is another useful suffix. Notice how it adds to the meaning of the root words in the following sentences.

1. The *judge* has just come in. We will know his *judgment* soon.
2. Joan was *excited*. We could see the *excitement* in her eyes.
3. Janet was *disappointed* by the news. Her *disappointment* showed on her face.

The *-ion* Suffix

Many words end in *-ion*. Often this suffix is added to a word without any change in spelling. It is easy to see the root word in *protection*. What is the root of *collection*? In some words the last *e* is dropped before adding *-ion*. The root of *operation* is *operate*. Notice how *ti* stands for /sh/. We say the last syllable in these words /shən/.

Sometimes, when the root words end with the sound of *n* or *m*, the suffix becomes *-ation*. You know that *combine* means "to put together." A *combination* means "things that are put together." Blue and yellow is a *combination* of colors that makes green. Say kom′bə·nā′shən.

97

You know the word *imagination*. Can you see the root word *imagine*?

What is the root word in *information*? If you *inform* someone of the news, do you give him *information*?

Try This

Find the root in each of the following words. Watch for changes in spelling.

direction	expansion	operation
subtraction	explanation	relation
collection	realization	punctuation
contraction		

What Did You Learn?

1. How are the words in a family related?
2. Build a word family. Use *love* as a root word. Your teacher will give you other words to build into families.
3. Why is it useful to know root words and suffixes?

America's Yesterdays

The Story of Christopher Columbus

Sailing the Sea of Darkness

Three wooden ships were ready. It would take ninety men to sail them. But who would want to sail over an unknown ocean? Most sailors thought the world was flat. They did not want to sail off the edge of the world.

100

How could Columbus get sailors for his ships? The King's soldiers forced some men to sign up. He got four more from the town jail. These men had to choose. They could stay in jail or they could sail with Columbus. They decided to take a chance with Columbus.

Some of the crew were young boys looking for adventure. Some were old sailors looking for gold.

Columbus made sure he had skilled men, too. There were doctors and able seamen.

At last everything was ready.

On board was a trunk piled full of things for trading with the natives. There were glass beads and red caps, rings and bells. There was salted meat and fish, and cheese to last a year. There was enough water to drink.

On the third day of August, in the year 1492, Christopher Columbus set sail from Spain. Three small wooden ships—the *Niña*, the *Pinta*, and the *Santa María*—sailed out over an unknown sea.

101

"Turn Back! Turn Back!"

Columbus kept a log, or diary, of the voyage. Each day he wrote how far he had sailed, what he had seen, and what had happened.

On the third day at sea there was trouble with the steering on the *Pinta*. They had to stop at a nearby island to fix it.

They sailed on, but they were still in sight of land. On September 6, the men saw fire and smoke rising from the top of a tall mountain. They were so frightened, they wanted to turn back at once. In a sure voice, Columbus told them that this was a volcano. He told them there was nothing to fear.

By September 9 they had sailed out of sight of land. For days they sailed. For weeks they sailed.

Never before had they sailed so long without seeing land. Most of the men were afraid.

"Turn back," they begged Columbus. "Turn back before the sea dragons eat us."

But Columbus was not afraid. He knew there were no sea dragons.

He tried to cheer up the sailors. He told them of the gold that would soon belong to them. He told them the King would give money to the first man who saw land.

But the men muttered and complained. The men complained when the wind blew too hard. They complained when there was no wind at all. And they complained about the weeds they saw in the sea.

"Many bunches of very green weeds," Columbus wrote in his log on September 16.

Some of the men were afraid the ships would get stuck in the thick green and yellow weeds. Columbus said the ships would sail right through. And they did.

On the night of September 25, a shout
came from the *Pinta*. "Land! Land, sir!
The reward is mine!"

Everyone shouted that he saw land.
Columbus fell to his knees and thanked
God.

That night no one slept. But in the
morning there was no land.

What they thought to be land was only a
low cloud. Columbus wrote in his diary
that what they had guessed to be land was
nothing but sky.

104

That day the men were more angry than ever. They said, "There is not much drinking water left. We will die of thirst. Let's throw Columbus overboard. We could say he fell in."

Columbus heard the men planning.

He said to them, "Kill me if you like. But it will do you no good. The King and Queen will hang every last one of you if you come home without me."

Then he said again that the first man to sight land would get a reward. "And I myself will give that man a fine jacket of silk," he said.

But these words did not comfort the frightened sailors. They kept a close watch on Columbus. They were still ready to kill him.

Columbus thought, "Land is near. I'm sure of it. But how can I make my men believe it?"

He begged them, "Give me three days. Only three days. If we do not see land by that time, I promise we shall sail home."

"Land! Land Ahead!"

All day Columbus watched for land.
Suddenly a group of birds flew overhead.
A branch with shiny leaves and flowers
floated by. Land must be near!

Now there was no more talk of turning
back. Now the sailors watched hopefully
for the first sight of land.

On the night of October 11, one hour
before moonrise, Christopher Columbus
thought he saw a light. Later he wrote it
was like "a little wax candle rising and
falling."

One minute he saw it.

The next minute it was gone.

Columbus stood on the deck for four hours watching and waiting.

The moon was bright. And the sails looked as if they were made of silver. It was two o'clock in the morning of October 12, 1492.

Suddenly a cry was heard in the quiet night: "Land! Land ahead!"

Christopher Columbus looked. He saw a sandy beach shining in the moonlight. And behind the beach was a forest of tall trees.

The voyage was over. It had taken sixty-nine days.

Quickly Columbus dressed in his best clothes. As soon as it was light enough, the men lowered the rowboats.

A few minutes later Columbus stood on the soil of a new land. He got down on his knees to kiss the ground.

As he gave thanks to God, tears of joy streamed down his face. He rose and planted the flag of Spain in the new land. He called the island San Salvador.

Looking for Gold

There were many natives on the island. Columbus called the natives Indians because he thought San Salvador was near India. He saw that the Indians were gentle and friendly.

But were these Indians the only people on the island? Where were their great cities? Where were the buildings with roofs of gold?

The only gold Columbus found on San Salvador were thin golden rings the natives wore in their noses and ears. In trade for this gold, Columbus and his men gave glass beads and red caps and bells. The Indians

told them in sign language that more gold
—much gold—could be found to the south.

For almost two weeks the men of the
Niña, the *Pinta*, and the *Santa María* sailed,
looking for gold. They found many beautiful
islands. They found strange birds and fish
and natives everywhere.

But they did not find gold.

On October 28, they reached the large
island of Cuba. Columbus wrote in his

diary that it gave him great joy to see "green
things and groves of trees and to hear the
birds sing."

But the King and Queen of Spain had not
asked Columbus to bring back trees and
singing birds. They wanted gold for Spain.

Columbus and his men kept on looking
for gold. They came to the beautiful island
of Haiti on December 6. Columbus named
it Hispaniola.

More than a thousand natives visited the
ships. Some came in boats. Others swam.

They brought many gifts for Columbus. They gave him fruit, cotton, and parrots. But it was the pieces of gold they brought that made Columbus the happiest. Now he was sure there was a rich gold mine on Hispaniola.

Columbus made up his mind. He would leave some men behind to look for the gold mine, while he and the rest of the crew returned to Spain.

There were rough storms at sea. But Columbus and his crew arrived safely back in Spain on March 15, 1493. The whole voyage had taken thirty-two weeks—almost eight months.

Columbus made three more voyages. He reached different parts of the Americas. But, although he found some gold, it was not much.

All his life he was sure he had reached islands near China and Japan and India. He never knew that he had found a whole new land instead.

And that land is America.

A Brave Explorer

A black man in worn knee pants and a hat stood on a high mesa in the blazing sun. He looked across a golden desert. Beyond the desert, as far as he could see, were only mountains.

The man was Estevan, called by his friends Estevanico. He was looking for the Seven Cities of Cibola that he had heard were built of gold. The Indians who showed him the way into the Southwest knew nothing about such cities. They simply wondered what this strange man was looking for and why he had come into this desert country.

Estevanico, whose Spanish name meant

114

Kid Steve, was born in Africa. He became an explorer, fearless and full of the love of adventure.

•He sailed from Spain with a group of five hundred men looking for new lands beyond the seas. They landed on the coast of Florida. But there, Indians and a strange sickness killed half of them in less than three months.

The men set sail again. This time their ship was wrecked. All the men were killed in the shipwreck except Estevanico and three Spaniards.

For more than eight years these four men wandered across the country, living with the Indians. Estevanico learned to speak many Indian languages. This helped him in his travels. He wandered as far south as Mexico City where he stayed for awhile.

But Estevanico did not like to stay in one place long. In 1539 he joined a group looking for the fabulous Seven Cities of Cibola. They set out northward over the mountains and across the plains.

Now he stood looking over the desert, wondering about the cities of gold. The summer was very hot, and before it was over the men were too tired to go on. They asked Estevanico if he would go ahead with a group of Indian runners. If he found rich lands or golden cities, they told him to send someone back with word and they would join him.

Since the Indian runners could not speak Spanish, Estevanico worked out a simple plan for sending back messages. He said he would send back a cross every few days. Its size would show how far he had gone and how important his discovery was.

A little wooden cross the size of the hand, made from twigs, would mean that he had found nothing special. But if he found cities of gold or fabulous riches, he would cut branches from a larger tree and send back a bigger cross.

At first the Indian runners brought back only very small crosses made of twigs. Estevanico was traveling across a rough and dangerous land where nobody lived. Heat, sand flies, mountain lions, cold nights, and blazing hot days made him go slowly. Dangerous animals ran through the rocky passes. There were a great many snakes.

Sometimes a blue racer rushed across his path, or he met a rattler in an angry coil.

But Estevanico kept on going across the sands, beyond the mountains. He kept looking for the gold and riches of the fabulous land he hoped was just ahead. Meanwhile, the other men waited for news from him.

One day two Indians, tired and worn out from the heat, came into the camp with a cross as tall as a man. Then the men knew that Estevanico had found a wonderful land somewhere in the desert. Perhaps he had even found the Seven Cities of Cibola!

Quickly the Spaniards broke camp. They followed the Indian runners toward the new country which the explorer, Estevanico, had discovered for them.

The Spaniards did not find any golden cities, but they did find great pueblos built by the Indians. They found houses sometimes as high as four stories. And they found what is now the state of Arizona.

But Estevanico was never seen again. The Indians had killed him. They had feared that other strangers might follow Estevanico into their land and take it away from them.

And that is just what happened in the end. The Spaniards said that the Indians' land belonged to Spain. It became a part of the New World—now Arizona and New Mexico—first discovered by Estevanico.

Map of the United States. The star shows the area discovered by Estevanico for Spain.

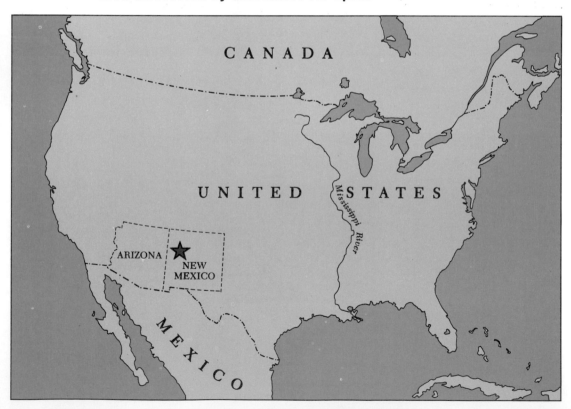

Pilgrim Thanksgiving

Damaris opened her eyes and sat up in bed, listening. Her heart beat hard, yet she did not know what had frightened her.

Then Damaris remembered. This was the day the Indians would come. Governor Bradford had invited the Indians to a feast of thanksgiving. The holiday was to last three days.

Damaris knew that she should be happy. During the first hard winter, there had not been enough food or enough houses. The Pilgrims had been cold and hungry and sick. Many had died.

Now the summer sun and air had helped them grow strong and well again. They had some houses built. The Indians had shown them how to plant corn. The crops had been gathered. There was enough food for everyone for the winter. Oh yes, there was certainly much to be thankful for. But Damaris wished the Indians had not been invited to the thanksgiving feast.

She heard her older brother, Giles, turn in his straw bed nearby. He sat up, rubbing his eyes. Then he saw her.

"Why are you sitting there shivering?" Giles asked.

"Something waked me," Damaris said.

"I thought it might be the Indians coming."

Giles laughed. "Are you still afraid of Indians?" he said. "The Indians are our friends — or Governor Bradford would not have invited them."

"Then why does Captain Standish keep marching the men up and down the hill? Why must Father and all the other men carry their guns wherever they go?"

"Maybe because of wolves," Giles said.

Damaris shook her head. She knew it was not because of wolves. "I heard Father talking," she said. "He says that many Indians fear us and would kill us if their chief, Massasoit, was not such a good true friend."

"Well, Massasoit is good and the Indians are our friends now," Giles said. "And we had better get up and help with the work or they will be here before we are ready."

Giles jumped out of bed and put on his clothes. Then he went down the ladder of logs nailed against the wall into the one room of the house.

Damaris could smell corn-meal porridge cooking for breakfast. She got out of bed, dressed, and then went down the rough ladder.

124

Her mother was feeding porridge to her baby brother who had been born on the *Mayflower*. He was a year old now.

"Do you think he knows this is our first holiday in this new land?" Damaris asked Mother.

Mother smiled. "Maybe he feels how excited we all are," she said. "Now we must hurry. The sun is shining. It's going to be a beautiful day. We must finish the cooking."

"That's what we've been doing for days," Damaris said.

Damaris hurried and ate her corn-meal porridge. Then she went to help the other children set the table outdoors. The men had built a long table of wooden boards in the clearing away from the houses. The houses were not big enough to hold all the guests for the feast.

As Damaris carried some corn pudding to the table, a little dog ran to meet her. He jumped up and barked. She held the pudding higher.

125

"No, no, Little Dog," she said. "You must wait. But I know how hungry you are."

Little Dog had come across the ocean on the *Mayflower* with Damaris. There had been only two dogs on the ship. This dog was the smaller so she had always called him Little Dog.

Little Dog stayed close to her. He ran about her feet so that she almost tripped over him as she carried dishes of food. But

she laughed. He was such a loving, funny little dog, even if he wasn't very brave.

Little Dog was afraid of loud noises. He was afraid of the sound of the drums and horn when Captain Standish marched the men. He was afraid of thunder. He was afraid of the wolves in the woods.

The other children sometimes laughed at him when he put his tail between his legs and ran.

But Damaris knew what it was to be afraid. She petted the little dog. He liked to hide under her long full skirts. Oh yes, from there, he looked out quite bravely.

Damaris went back and forth from the house with food. Then, from the woods, came the sound of a trumpet, then a drum. *Rat-a-tat-tat! Rum-dee-dee-dum-dum-dum!*

Little Dog put his tail between his legs. He ran for Damaris. She could feel him shaking against her feet. She looked toward the woods. Her own heart beat faster. The Indians were coming.

The Indians Arrive

Earlier that morning, Captain Standish and a group of Pilgrim men had gone to meet the Indians. Now, the drum sounds came nearer. *Rat-a-tat-tat! Rum-dee-dum-dum-dum!*

Mothers came from the houses. Children ran to stand near the table. All looked toward the woods.

Captain Standish came from the woods first. He was not so tall as the other men, but he was straight and fearless. Behind

him came a few Pilgrim men with guns.
Then came the Indians.

Their chief, Massasoit, led them. He was
tall and walked proudly. Behind him came
Indian men. Some of them carried wild
turkey and deer meat for the feast.

The Indians wore leggings and a kind of
shirt made of deerskin. Their hair was
very black and long. It was cut off in
front so that it would not hang in their
eyes. Their faces were painted in a wide
stripe from the forehead down to the chin.
They carried bows and arrows and
tomahawks.

They kept coming from the woods and coming from the woods. Damaris could not count fast enough to know how many there were. But she knew there were certainly many more Indians than Pilgrims. There were only twenty white men and six growing boys left in all the Pilgrim village. There were a few women. More than half the Pilgrims were children. And all these Indians who came were tall, straight men.

Damaris heard her brother Giles counting softly. Then he said to his friend Richard, who stood beside him, "I counted ninety."

"A few of their braves do not look much older than we are," Richard said.

"Perhaps they were allowed to come because they are good at the races and dances," Giles said. "Father says the Indians will do some of their dances after the dinner. See that young brave with the wildcat tail around his neck. He is about my size. I will try to make friends with him."

Little Dog looked out from under

Damaris' skirt. Damaris patted his head.

"Don't you wish we were as brave as my brother Giles?" she said softly to the little dog.

When the welcome was over, the women and children hurried to put the food upon the long table. The men began to sit down on benches at the table. Chief Massasoit and Governor Bradford sat at the head. A few of the older Indian braves sat at the table with the Pilgrim men. Most of the Indians sat on the ground.

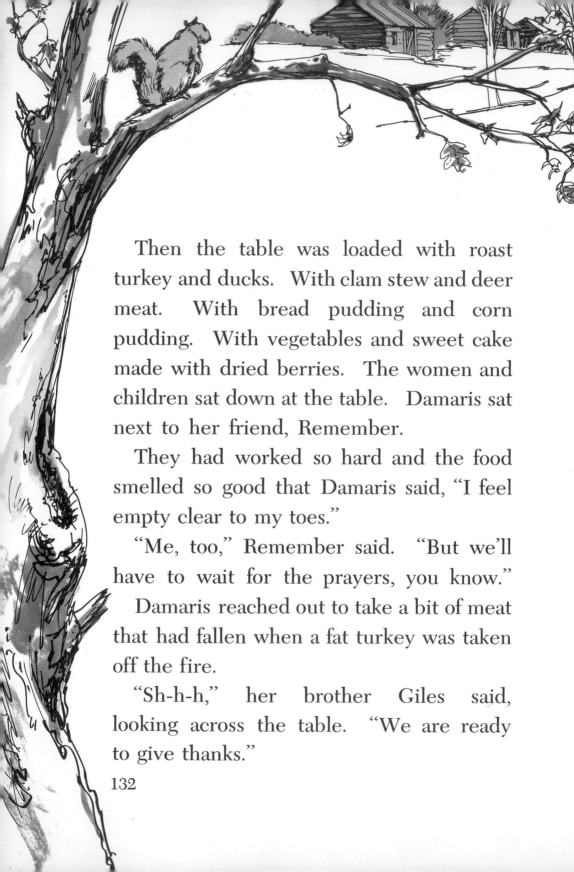

Then the table was loaded with roast turkey and ducks. With clam stew and deer meat. With bread pudding and corn pudding. With vegetables and sweet cake made with dried berries. The women and children sat down at the table. Damaris sat next to her friend, Remember.

They had worked so hard and the food smelled so good that Damaris said, "I feel empty clear to my toes."

"Me, too," Remember said. "But we'll have to wait for the prayers, you know."

Damaris reached out to take a bit of meat that had fallen when a fat turkey was taken off the fire.

"Sh-h-h," her brother Giles said, looking across the table. "We are ready to give thanks."

132

Damaris lowered her head quickly. For a long time she kept her eyes almost closed as the prayers were said. How good everything smelled. How long the prayers lasted. She was so hungry.

Then across from her she saw Giles' friend, Richard. His head was bowed. There was a thankful look on his face. She knew he was thankful for food, good crops, and friends.

Damaris bowed her head again and said to herself, "Thank Thee, dear God, for my good mother and father, for my brother Giles and my baby brother and my sister—for everything."

She felt a warm furry body stir against her feet.

"And thank Thee, too, for Little Dog and his funny ways that make us laugh," she added.

Damaris saw how quietly the Indians listened to the prayers although they could not understand a word. They seemed to know that this was the white man's way of saying thank you to the Great Father who takes care of all people, red and white.

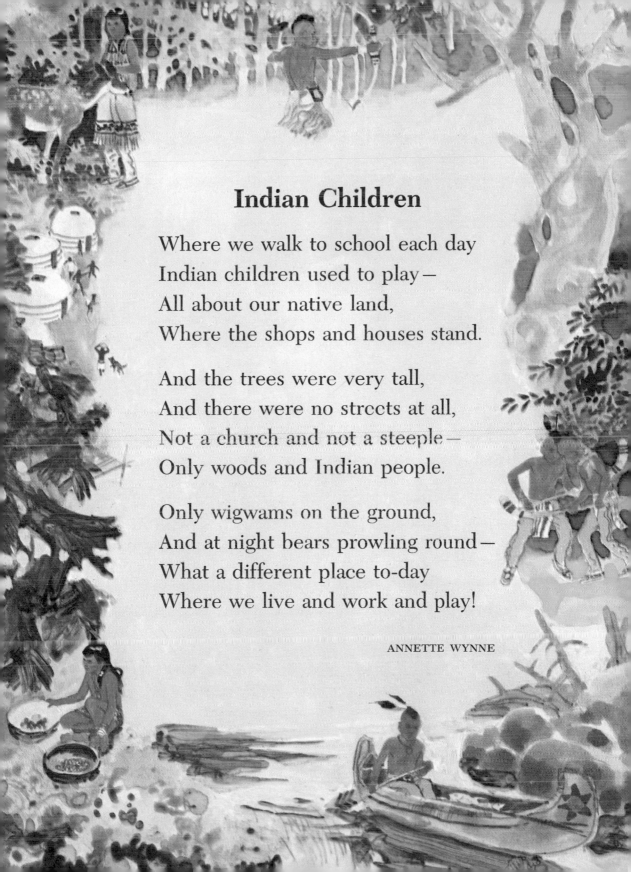

Indian Children

Where we walk to school each day
Indian children used to play—
All about our native land,
Where the shops and houses stand.

And the trees were very tall,
And there were no streets at all,
Not a church and not a steeple—
Only woods and Indian people.

Only wigwams on the ground,
And at night bears prowling round—
What a different place to-day
Where we live and work and play!

ANNETTE WYNNE

Daniel Boone and Chief Blackfish

The housewives in Boonesborough needed salt. Daniel Boone had to get it, even though the trip would be dangerous. The British were paying the Indians to make attacks on the white men. Besides, it was winter. Footprints would show plainly in the snow, and Indians could see them.

Nevertheless, Daniel led thirty men to a spring of salt water that he knew about. There they camped and boiled the water down in pots to get the salt.

136

That day Boone left the others at work while he hunted alone for fresh meat. Suddenly a party of Shawnee Indians appeared on all sides of him. They took him unharmed to their camp. There he discovered a hundred fully armed Indians, and a number of white men sent by the British.

This could only mean that an attack on Boonesborough, Daniel's village, was planned. What could Daniel do? While he was thinking, the Shawnees crowded around him. He was such a special prisoner that they all wanted to shake his hand!

"Howdy," Boone said to their chief, Blackfish.

"Howdy," Blackfish answered without smiling. "My men have seen your group making salt."

Now Daniel had even more to think about. This big party of Indians might capture or kill the salt-makers. Then they would fall upon Boonesborough. The British had promised a reward for any pioneers—or their scalps.

"I will tell my men to surrender, if you promise not to harm them," Boone said to Blackfish.

Blackfish agreed, and Daniel was sure he would keep his word.

Now Daniel said cleverly, "You will have

138

many prisoners. It will be hard to take women and children with you in this cold weather. It is wiser to wait and capture Boonesborough in the spring."

Blackfish nodded. "I will leave the women and children till spring," he said. "But if the salt-makers do not surrender peacefully, you will be killed."

Boone went back and talked to his friends at the salt spring. They agreed there was nothing they could do but surrender. Through the snow they all marched off, toward the British camp.

Boone Becomes a Shawnee

Chief Blackfish took a great liking to Daniel Boone. He liked Boone so much that he would not sell him to the British, even though the British would give a big reward for him. Instead, he called Boone his own son and treated him with kindness.

Boone pretended to become a good Shawnee. He allowed his long hair to be pulled out like a Shawnee's, leaving only a small scalp piece. Although he didn't like this part of Shawnee life, there were many

other things that he liked and enjoyed. But when he saw his "father," Blackfish, getting ready for war on Boonesborough, he knew the time had come to run away. He must keep the Indians from guessing his plan, and he did so in a very clever way.

When a group of hunters weren't looking, Boone slipped the bullets out of their guns, but left the powder in. He hid the bullets under his shirt.

"Brothers, I am going home," he called to them suddenly. And he started off.

"You are not going!" Blackfish shouted. "If you try, I will shoot you."

Boone kept on walking.

True to his word, Blackfish picked up his gun. So did the others. As they fired, Boone held his hand in the air and pretended to be catching the bullets. After the smoke cleared away, there stood Daniel unharmed. In his hand were the bullets he had "caught" — the same ones he had taken from the Indians' guns a few minutes before.

"Here are your bullets," he said to the surprised Blackfish. "Boone ain't going away."

The trick worked like magic—which the Shawnees thought it was. They grew careless and didn't watch Daniel as closely as they had before.

One day he saw his chance when all the men were out hunting turkeys. Only the Indian women were in their camp. He grabbed a horse, said goodbye to his Shawnee "mother," and rode off for home.

Boone rode until his horse was nearly dead. Then he ran and walked the rest of the way. In four days he covered one hundred and sixty miles.

The warning Daniel brought saved Boonesborough. The people there had time enough to get ready for the attack. Although they were outnumbered seven to one, they were able to fight off the war party.

Later, attacks on the pioneers died down. Before long Boone left Boonesborough and went farther west where he lived to be almost eighty-six years old.

Daniel Boone 1735-1820

When Daniel Boone goes by at night
The phantom deer arise
And all lost, wild America
Is burning in their eyes.

ROSEMARY AND STEPHEN VINCENT BENÉT

Topics of Paragraphs

Phil was reading a book about weather. He was going to make a report to his class, and he wanted to remember the important ideas. He decided to write down the topic of each paragraph. The topics would help him to remember what the paragraphs were about. Then he could tell in his own words the ideas in the paragraph.

Here is one paragraph that Phil read. As you read it, think of what most of the sentences tell about. Then, on a piece of paper, write *Weather* for a title. Under it write A, and beside A write what you think the topic is.

A

I *Weather*
A.
B.
C.
D.

Weather plays an important part in most people's lives. Farmers need good weather to grow their crops. Storms or a sudden frost can kill vegetables and fruits. Then we have to pay more money for the food we eat.

144

Rain and snow may be bad for storekeepers because few people go shopping in stormy weather. Snow makes buses, trains, and planes late. Fog keeps planes from flying. You can probably think of other ways that weather affects what people do.

Phil knew that "weather" would not be the right topic. The whole book was about weather! Paragraph A must tell only one thing about weather.

When Phil read the first sentence, he had a good idea what the paragraph would tell. But he could not be sure until he had read all the other sentences. Each sentence explained a bit more about the part weather plays in people's lives. When Phil read the last sentence in Paragraph A, he was sure of the topic. He wrote, "How weather affects people's lives." Is your topic like Phil's?

When he read the next paragraph, Phil asked himself, "What does the first sentence tell?" He decided that the first sentence explains the word *forecasts*. The rest of the paragraph would probably tell about weather forecasts.

Read Paragraph B and see if Phil's guess was right. On your paper write B and the topic. Is the topic given in one sentence? Which one?

B

Weather forecasts tell people what kind of weather to expect. When the weatherman forecasts an early frost, the farmer can protect his oranges. If the cowboy knows that a snowstorm is coming, he may be able to get his herd to shelter. When a hurricane is forecast, people can move out of its way. The weatherman's forecast may save thousands of lives and millions of dollars.

For the topic of Paragraph B, Phil wrote, "How weather forecasts help people." Do you agree that this is the topic? If you do, you know that the last sentence in the paragraph gives the topic.

Try This

Here are two more paragraphs from Phil's book on weather. As you read, think of what topic most of the sentences tell about. Then, on your paper, beside C and D, write the topics of these two paragraphs.

C

For many years people have tried to change the weather. Long ago, Indians would dance and pray to bring rain to make their corn grow. Today farmers send an airplane to "seed" a cloud to make rain. Sometimes "seeding" helps to get rid of fog or wind or hail, which may hurt fruit trees. Someday men may learn how to change the direction of a hurricane.

D

To make forecasts, weathermen collect information on the weather from many different places. They get reports from all parts of the United States and Canada. Men in airplanes report the weather by radio. Reports come in from ships on the oceans. Some weather information comes from balloons that go very high into the sky.

Have you written the topics for C and D on your piece of paper? If so, you have made an *outline* just as Phil did for his report. His outline looked like this:

I. Weather
    A. How weather affects people's lives
    B. How weather forecasts help people
    C. How people try to change the weather
    D. Collecting weather information

Does your outline look like Phil's? If it is different, can you explain why? Which outline do you think is better?

What Did You Learn?
1. How do you find the topic of a paragraph?
2. You made an outline of the four paragraphs on weather. How might you use an outline like this?

Friends Along the Way

The Case of the Rubber Pillow

During the summer, Encyclopedia Brown worked as a detective for children who lived in the neighborhood. He opened his office every morning after his father left for work.

Encyclopedia always waited till his father drove off. He had to. His office was in the garage.

After his father left, he put out his sign:

DETECTIVE
ANDREW BROWN
13 BEECH AVENUE
No case too small
25¢ a day

Late in the morning Danny, a neighbor, ran into Detective Brown's office. He put down his money on the table beside Encyclopedia.

"I want you to find my pillow," said Danny. "It's missing."

"I've seen a match box and a boardwalk, but I've never worked on a pillowcase," said Encyclopedia thoughtfully.

"My pillow doesn't have a case," said Danny. "It's made of rubber. I blow it up on camping trips."

"Hmm," said Encyclopedia. "It gave you the air. When?"

"Half an hour ago," said Danny. "I think Bugs Meany took it."

"Bugs?" At that Encyclopedia became serious.

Bugs Meany was known to be a trouble maker.

"I'll take the case," said Encyclopedia. "Let's have the whole story."

"Early this morning," said Danny, "Dad and I were painting the wood on the front of our house—the three front steps, the porch railing and posts, and the front door. We painted everything white."

"Where was the rubber pillow?" asked Encyclopedia.

"It was hanging on the clothesline at the side of the house," said Danny. "After

152

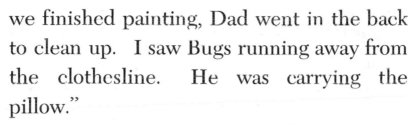

we finished painting, Dad went in the back to clean up. I saw Bugs running away from the clothesline. He was carrying the pillow."

"Did your father see him, too?"

"No, bad luck," said Danny. "It will be my word against Bugs's."

Encyclopedia closed his eyes. For several minutes he did some deep thinking.

Then he said, "We've got to trap Bugs. We've got to catch him in a lie!"

"It won't be easy," said Danny. "He's a smart fellow."

The two boys rode their bikes to Bugs's hangout, an unused tool shed behind Mr. Henry's Fix-It Shop.

Bugs was there. He was alone, playing with a deck of cards.

"Beat it," he said.

"I will when you return Danny's pillow," said Encyclopedia.

"You took my rubber pillow from the clothesline at my house half an hour ago," said Danny.

"*Rubber* pillow? Man, has this kid's mouth heard from his brain lately?" barked Bugs. "I've never been near his house in my life."

"Why don't you tell that to Danny's father?" said Encyclopedia. "He was behind the house. He must have seen you take the pillow."

Bugs nearly choked on the blade of grass he was chewing. He recovered himself and said, "I've been right here all morning."

"Then you wouldn't mind going with us to Danny's house," said Encyclopedia. "You're going to have to speak with his father sooner or later."

"W-well, ahh, O.K.," muttered Bugs.

154

"But you lead the way. Remember, I don't even know where he lives."

Outside, Danny whispered, "My father went off fishing. My mother is shopping. There's nobody at home."

"Don't worry," said Encyclopedia. "Bugs is far too sure of himself. He'll make a mistake."

The three boys rode over to Danny's house. It was a green house with a white wood porch, door, and front steps.

"Go up and ring the doorbell," Encyclopedia dared Bugs.

Bugs kicked down the stand of his bike. He looked at Danny's house. He looked at Danny. He seemed to be getting up his nerve. Suddenly he made up his mind.

"Watch me," he said.

He ran across the front yard and leaped over the three white wood steps. His heel hit the floor of the porch. He tripped, but righted himself without having to grab the railing. He looked back at Danny and Encyclopedia and grinned.

When he got no answer to the doorbell, Bugs walked a step to the window that faced onto the porch. He rapped on the glass several times.

"There's nobody home," he yelled to Encyclopedia. He left the porch, again leaping over the three steps.

"Your plan to trap him didn't work," said Danny.

"Oh, yes it did!" said Encyclopedia.

He went to Bugs and spoke into the bigger boy's left ear.

Bugs listened. His fists tightened. Angry stars seemed to shoot from his ears. Low, fighting sounds rolled in his throat.

But he said, "Awh. . . ."

He got on his bike, a beaten fellow. Five minutes later he was back with Danny's rubber pillow.

"What did you say to him?" asked Danny, after Bugs had gone off.

"Not very much. I simply pointed out his mistake," said the boy detective. "In this case, what he did spoke louder than what he said."

WHAT WAS BUGS'S MISTAKE?

Answer to The Case of the Rubber Pillow

Bugs said he had never been to Danny's house. Yet he didn't touch the porch railing, the steps, and the front door. He knew they had just been painted and were still wet.

Operation Rescue

Sleet and rain were still hitting against the windows when June Sloan woke up. She lay in her bed and listened to the wind as it roared in the trees. June sighed as she sat up in bed to look at her friend, Wendy, who was sleeping in the other bed across the room.

"You awake yet, Wendy?" she asked softly.

The covers moved and Wendy turned over. Stretching her arms, she asked, "Still raining?"

"Yes, it's still raining and sleeting — hard," answered June. "But let's get up and see what's going on anyway."

159

She sat on the edge of the bed and let her feet touch the soft, warm back of her dog, Big Sam. The dog was stretched out comfortably on the floor beside her bed.

"Come on, Sam, you sleepy head. Time to get up and out for your morning walk."

Big Sam opened his large brown eyes and looked up at June. He rubbed against her feet and closed his eyes again. He could hear the rain outside too!

June finally had to give Big Sam a push to get him to go outdoors for his morning run.

160

"What a funny dog," said Wendy. "He loves water to swim in, but he sure hates to go out in the rain."

"I would too, especially today," June said. "It's pretty nasty outside. Even the meadow back of the house is getting flooded. He won't wander far. He's a fair-weather dog at heart."

"Wish it was fair weather right now," said Wendy, as the girls headed for the kitchen where Mrs. Sloan was cooking breakfast.

June didn't say anything. She had been so excited when her mother said that Wendy could visit her during the winter holidays.

Wendy lived in the city. She had never stayed at the seashore after the summer. June's family lived at the seashore all year around. June had planned all the exciting places she and Wendy could explore during her visit. But the day Wendy got there, the cold rain and sleet had set in. For three nasty days now the girls had

161

hardly been able to get out of the house.

Just as the two girls finished their breakfast, they heard Big Sam at the back door.

"What's the matter with him?" wondered June. "He usually barks to come in." She opened the door and Big Sam trotted in, his wet tail wagging excitedly. He dropped a bundle of feathers at June's feet.

"What's that?" Wendy asked. "It's moving!"

"I don't know," said June. "Looks like some kind of bird."

As the small bundle of feathers shook itself, a head and bill appeared, followed by two short wings.

"It's a baby penguin," shouted Wendy.

"Can't be," June said. "There aren't any penguins around here." She bent down and gently touched the head of the little black and white bird. It poked its bill weakly at her hand. Then it started to run around the kitchen, wobbling and rolling as it went.

"He can hardly walk," Wendy said. "His legs are funny—too short, or something."

Then the little bird started for the kitchen door. With one leap, Big Sam landed beside the bird, very gently picked him up, and put him at June's feet again. The bird lay flat for a moment. He hardly moved when June carefully picked him up and held him in her hand.

"Oh, a dovekie!" exclaimed Mrs. Sloan when she saw the bird in June's hands. "Where in the world did he come from?"

Big Sam gave a sharp bark, his tail thumping against the floor. The girls laughed.

"He's trying to tell you that he found the bird," June said. "It must have been on the sea meadow."

The Day Brightens

"What's a dovekie?" asked Wendy. "I never heard of them."

"Dovekies are birds that live mostly on the ocean," answered Mrs. Sloan. "They come down from the very cold lands in winter, looking for food. But I wonder why he was out here, a half mile from the beach."

"May I keep him?" June asked. "We can build him a nice cage."

"Oh, no, dear. That would never do," said Mrs. Sloan. "A dovekie must have the ocean to dive in for his food. He would probably never eat from your hand."

June and Wendy looked at each other. For a moment they'd thought there was going to be something exciting to do.

"Shall I just put him outside then?" asked June.

"No," her mother said. "He very likely was blown inland by the storm and came down on the meadow near the beach because he couldn't fly any farther. He wouldn't be strong enough to get up enough speed to fly from land."

"Poor little thing," said Wendy. "I wish we could help you, little dovekie."

"There is something you girls can do," Mrs. Sloan said. "You can take the dovekie to the beach and put him in the water. But first put on your rain gear."

All of a sudden the weather didn't matter at all to June and Wendy. They put the little bird in a corner of the kitchen and fixed two chairs to pen him in. The dovekie looked up at the girls and blinked. Then he went into the corner and turned his back on them. The girls and Mrs. Sloan laughed. The bird looked like a bad little boy ordered to stand in the corner.

When the girls had on their rain things, June picked up the dovekie. The bird rested comfortably in her gloves.

They went out and followed the road to the beach, along the edge of the sea meadow. Big Sam ran back and forth excitedly from the road to the meadow. They hadn't gone far when he returned from one of his runs across the meadow and proudly dropped another small bundle of feathers at June's feet.

"Another dovekie!" June exclaimed, as she picked up the little bird and held it gently in her hands. "Where's he finding them?"

The girls looked over at the meadow from where Big Sam had come.

"Look over there," cried Wendy. "I can see lots of dovekies."

Big Sam ran back twice for other dovekies and brought them to the girls.

"We'd better take these to the beach," said June. "Then we can come back and look for more."

168

June and Wendy each carried two dovekies and Sam carried one. The big dog seemed especially proud of his little bundle. He took great care to be gentle as he trotted along with the girls.

The girls carried the birds to the very edge of the water and then let them go. The dovekies quickly went into the water and swam a few feet off shore. Then they all dived down and disappeared underneath the icy water.

"Hey, look!" called Wendy. "They've gone under water."

"But they'll have to come up again soon," June said. The girls waited for what seemed a long time. All they could see was the great stretch of empty gray ocean.

"There they are way out there!" Wendy shouted as four little black spots appeared —pop, pop, pop, pop—one right after the other.

Then June realized that Big Sam, standing quietly beside her, was still holding his dovekie.

"Let him go, Big Sam," June ordered him. The black dog lowered his head and carefully opened his mouth. The little bird dropped easily into the sand. For a

moment it lay there, not realizing it was
free. Then it jumped up on its strange
little legs, a little wobbly, and headed
right for the water. Soon, it was just a
dark spot with the others, now quite far
from the shore.

"Let's go back and see if Sam can find
some more dovekies," Wendy said.

"O.K.," June agreed. "If he does, we'll
bring them back to the water, too."

"Boy, is this fun!" said Wendy. "I
never was in a real rescue operation before."

"It sure is," said June. "Come on, Big
Sam. On with 'operation rescue.'"

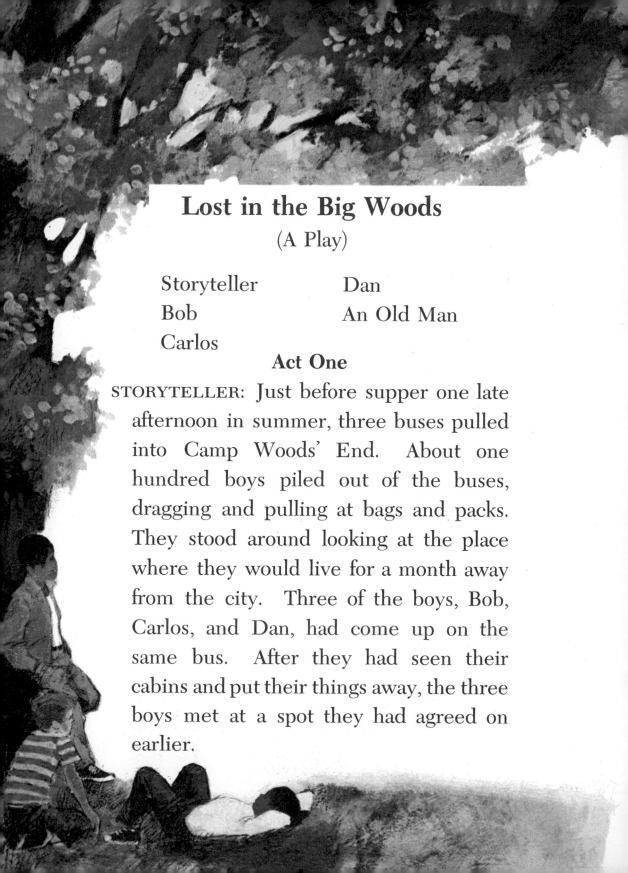

Lost in the Big Woods
(A Play)

Storyteller   Dan
Bob   An Old Man
Carlos

Act One

STORYTELLER: Just before supper one late afternoon in summer, three buses pulled into Camp Woods' End. About one hundred boys piled out of the buses, dragging and pulling at bags and packs. They stood around looking at the place where they would live for a month away from the city. Three of the boys, Bob, Carlos, and Dan, had come up on the same bus. After they had seen their cabins and put their things away, the three boys met at a spot they had agreed on earlier.

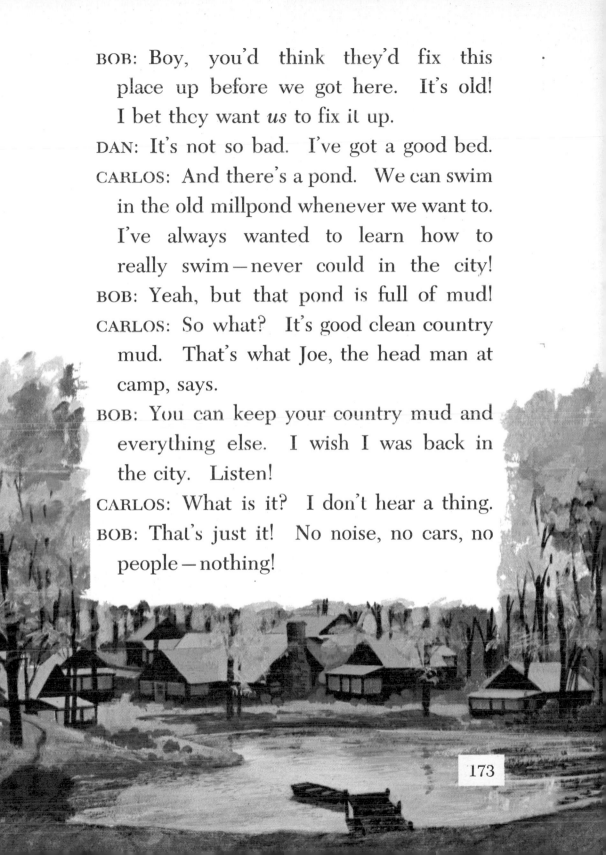

BOB: Boy, you'd think they'd fix this place up before we got here. It's old! I bet they want *us* to fix it up.

DAN: It's not so bad. I've got a good bed.

CARLOS: And there's a pond. We can swim in the old millpond whenever we want to. I've always wanted to learn how to really swim—never could in the city!

BOB: Yeah, but that pond is full of mud!

CARLOS: So what? It's good clean country mud. That's what Joe, the head man at camp, says.

BOB: You can keep your country mud and everything else. I wish I was back in the city. Listen!

CARLOS: What is it? I don't hear a thing.

BOB: That's just it! No noise, no cars, no people—nothing!

173

DAN: Then why did you come?

BOB: Oh, my mother put my name in, and she kept going on about all that "good old country air."

STORYTELLER: The boys started walking down a dirt path. Before they knew it they were wandering farther and farther into the woods.

DAN: Hey fellows, where are we going?

BOB: I don't know, and I don't care. Maybe if we walk far enough, we'll run right into a town.

CARLOS: Maybe, but there sure aren't any towns near here.

DAN: Let's go back. We've wandered too far from camp.

BOB: What's the matter? You scared? Just turn yourself around and start walking. There's the path. Help yourself!

DAN: Where? I don't see any path.

BOB: Huh? What happened to it?

STORYTELLER: The boys looked around. In every direction the woods stretched, tall and dark.

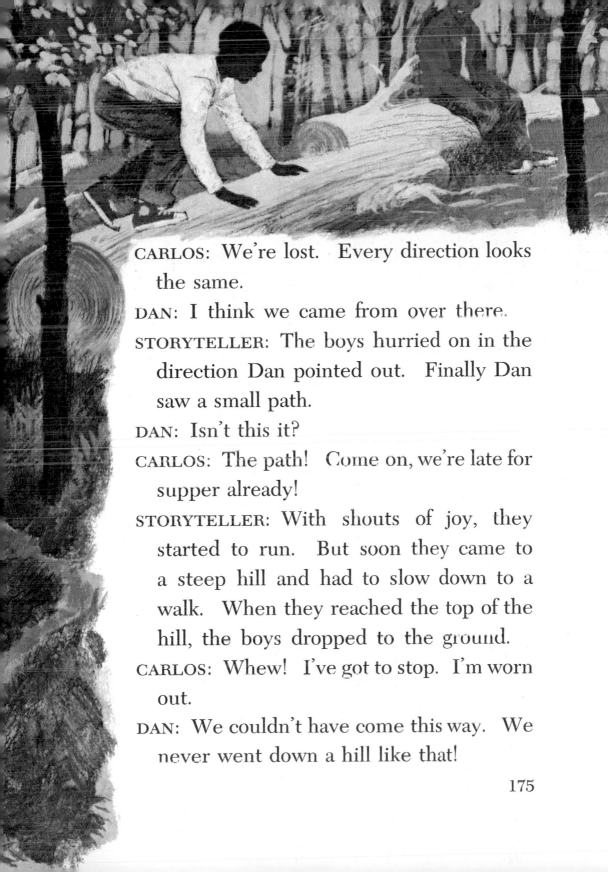

CARLOS: We're lost. Every direction looks the same.

DAN: I think we came from over there.

STORYTELLER: The boys hurried on in the direction Dan pointed out. Finally Dan saw a small path.

DAN: Isn't this it?

CARLOS: The path! Come on, we're late for supper already!

STORYTELLER: With shouts of joy, they started to run. But soon they came to a steep hill and had to slow down to a walk. When they reached the top of the hill, the boys dropped to the ground.

CARLOS: Whew! I've got to stop. I'm worn out.

DAN: We couldn't have come this way. We never went down a hill like that!

175

CARLOS: Let's face it. We're lost.

BOB: Oh, great! In the middle of the woods with no food, no fire, and no place to sleep! And getting too dark to go anywhere.

CARLOS: Do you think they'll look for us? They must have missed us by now.

DAN: Maybe, although they don't know where to look. And they might have to stop looking when it gets too dark.

BOB: You mean we'll have to stay here all night?

CARLOS: Oh, it's not so bad. And anyway, there's our bed, right up there. See that grove of pine trees?

BOB: Yeah, pine trees, I see them. But how do you make a bed out of them?

176

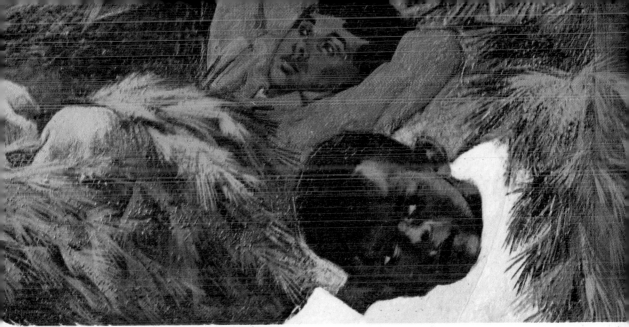

CARLOS: Well, I saw a show about camping on T.V. A man was showing how you can make a bed out of pine needles and branches and stuff. Boy, I never thought I'd really be doing it.

STORYTELLER: When they reached the pine grove, Carlos showed Dan and Bob how to pile pine needles in an open space to make a soft bed. Then he told them to break off some of the green pine branches to cover themselves with. When the boys finished their beds, they crawled into them. They lay on their backs, looking up at the sky, tired, but not quite ready for sleep.

CARLOS: Not bad, if I do say so. These branches really keep you warm.

BOB: You know, I'm going to be ready for breakfast by morning.

DAN: Don't talk about food!

BOB: Why not? Maybe there's a lunch counter just around that next corner. I can just picture it. There's a nice little old lady waiting for us with a pile of food—thick ham and cheese sandwiches and lots of mustard on them—hot apple turnovers—

DAN: You're dreaming. Go to sleep.

BOB: Hey, look at the sky! The stars are out. I can see all the way down the hill.

CARLOS: It isn't just the stars. The moon is coming up.

DAN: Bet you couldn't do this in the city.

BOB: Well, no, I guess not.

STORYTELLER: For a while the boys lay quietly in the stillness that was so new to them. Then, one by one, they closed their eyes and fell asleep.

178

Act Two

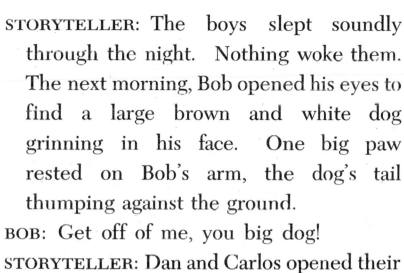

STORYTELLER: The boys slept soundly through the night. Nothing woke them. The next morning, Bob opened his eyes to find a large brown and white dog grinning in his face. One big paw rested on Bob's arm, the dog's tail thumping against the ground.

BOB: Get off of me, you big dog!

STORYTELLER: Dan and Carlos opened their eyes. Dan smiled at the sight of the dog.

DAN: He must live near here.

BOB: Maybe he belongs to that nice little old lady with thick ham and cheese sandwiches. Let's follow him.

STORYTELLER: The dog ran ahead and the boys followed him up a hill and down a path into a vegetable garden. At the other end of the garden was a tiny cabin with its door open.

BOB: Look, he's going in the cabin. And I can smell something cooking! It doesn't look like a lunch counter, but maybe —

STORYTELLER: Just then a man's voice boomed out from the cabin.

OLD MAN: Come on in, breakfast's ready!

STORYTELLER: The boys piled into the cabin and stopped just inside to stare at an old man with white hair.

OLD MAN: Well, what are you waiting for? Sit! It's blueberry pancakes. Picked the berries yesterday. Come on, they'll get cold.

DAN: But—But you had them all ready for us! How did you know we were coming?

OLD MAN: Oh, it wasn't very difficult. Last night about sundown, I was sitting out back, underneath the stars. Heard you fellows in my pines. Sound carries in the woods. Besides, the way the path turns, I was almost sitting next to you. Said to myself, "They'll be all right. I've slept in the woods lots of times myself on hot nights." Made up my mind to give you breakfast this morning, though. Pancakes good?

BOB: Good? They're great!

180

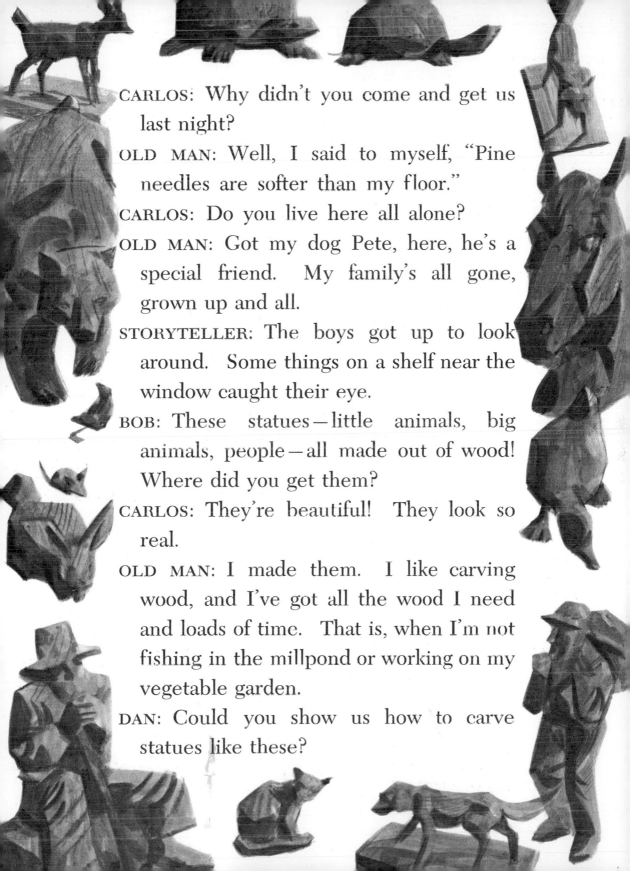

CARLOS: Why didn't you come and get us last night?

OLD MAN: Well, I said to myself, "Pine needles are softer than my floor."

CARLOS: Do you live here all alone?

OLD MAN: Got my dog Pete, here, he's a special friend. My family's all gone, grown up and all.

STORYTELLER: The boys got up to look around. Some things on a shelf near the window caught their eye.

BOB: These statues—little animals, big animals, people—all made out of wood! Where did you get them?

CARLOS: They're beautiful! They look so real.

OLD MAN: I made them. I like carving wood, and I've got all the wood I need and loads of time. That is, when I'm not fishing in the millpond or working on my vegetable garden.

DAN: Could you show us how to carve statues like these?

CARLOS: To make something like that — it would be wonderful.

BOB: I bet it's difficult. But I'd like to learn how to do it, too.

OLD MAN: Easy, now! It takes time to learn how to carve well. But I've got a class in woodcarving at your camp in a half hour. You can start learning then.

BOB: At camp! But we're miles from camp!

OLD MAN: You're in luck. It's just a short way from here. I've got a path that will get us to camp in two minutes.

BOB: Well, what are we waiting for? Let's go!

The People

The ants are walking under the ground,
And the pigeons are flying over the steeple,
And in between are the people.

ELIZABETH MADOX ROBERTS

The Two Cats

I'm very good friends with
      both our cats,
I've known them since they
      were kittens.
And one is little and one has
      big paws,
And their names are Midget
      and Mittens.

But sometimes at dusk when
      we're driving home
And come on the cats by surprise,
I feel a shiver go down my back
Facing their burning eyes.

ELIZABETH COATSWORTH

Every Time I Climb a Tree

Every time I climb a tree
Every time I climb a tree
Every time I climb a tree
I scrape a leg
Or skin a knee
And every time I climb a tree
I find some ants
Or dodge a bee
And get the ants
All over me.

And every time I climb a tree
Where have you been?
They say to me
But don't they know that I am free
Every time I climb a tree?

I like it best
To spot a nest
That has an egg
Or maybe three.

And then I skin
The other leg
But every time I climb a tree
I see a lot of things to see
Swallows rooftops and TV
And all the fields and farms there be
Every time I climb a tree
Though climbing may be good for ants
It isn't awfully good for pants
But still it's pretty good for me
Every time I climb a tree.

DAVID McCORD

A Little Happy Music

"UmmmmMMMH, I know what *we're* having for supper!" Idella said, dancing in through the door. She was not talking to anyone special, just saying it out loud when she smelled such a nice smell. She stopped at the kitchen to enjoy the nice smell.

Her mother grinned at Idella. "Hi, Sweetheart," she said.

"Hello, Mamma. Say, what's that funny noise?" Idella asked. But before her mother could answer, Idella was hurrying to the living room to find out for herself.

186

As soon as she saw her older brother, she walked toward him saying, "Now where did *that* come from, Kenny?"

"Quiet, Squirt. You're not supposed to butt in when somebody's making music."

"It doesn't sound like any music to me," she said, "and don't call me 'Squirt.' You're not so big yourself, you know. Where did we get that piano?" Idella still wanted to know.

"It came from a neighbor of Gramma," Kenny answered and went right on pushing down many different keys, pretending it was all very important. "The lady is moving away—and she sold it to Gramma. And Gramma said we could keep it. I helped some men move it up here this afternoon and now I'm playing it. If you act right," he said in a deep voice, "I'll even let you help me."

"Thank you very much," she kidded him right back. "And take off your hat in the house."

"O.K.," he said as he stood up to slide the telephone book close to one end of the

187

bench and sat on it again. "You play that side and I'll play this side and we'll have a concert."

So Idella stood at the other end of the piano and they began—tink-tank-KLONK!

It was fun making the strange sounds. Kenny would swing his arms way up in the air and lean back with his chin up and his eyes shut. Idella began to wiggle and do a little dance as she played.

It was an old, old piano. The paint was worn off in places. It had a strange and good smell. The white keys were yellowed. They were rubbed down and rounded at the edges. Idella liked to touch them because they were so warm and smooth.

The three pedals at the bottom of the piano were worn shiny. Kenny could step on any one of them if he stretched out his leg. There was one pedal to make the sound loud. Another was for soft. The pedal in the middle didn't seem to be good for anything.

Bing! Bang! ZONK!

Before very long their mother was calling to them from the kitchen, "Will you two please not play so loud or the neighbors will be ringing our bell."

"See, Kenny?" Idella said. "You can't play. You're not making music, you're just making a lot of noise!"

"Okay, Squirt," said Kenny, upset with his sister, "just for that, you can't help me with my concert!"

"I don't care if I ever help you make noise," she said. "And stop playing so loud! You heard what Mamma said. There, you hear that? Now one of the neighbors is banging on the pipes!"

Their mother came in from the kitchen to scold them. "I told you both! Now, you quiet down! I'm not going to tell you again! Oh, and there's your daddy at the door."

"Hi, Dad," they both sang out and ran to meet him. They wanted to show him the piano.

"Hello, *hello*, hello," he said. "See who
I met down the street."

"Oh, it's Uncle Charles!"

"Hi, Uncle Charles! Guess what we got
today!"

"Hold on a minute," their father said,
"and let your uncle at least get in the door."

"Hi, my friends," their uncle said,
swinging Idella up in his arms. "Hi,
Cookie. How're you?"

"When did you get back in town?" their
mother asked. She was happy to see her
brother again.

"Just this morning," Uncle Charles answered. "The band I'm working with just finished that job we had in Canada. Now we're supposed to work here in town this weekend."

"That's fine," she said, and turned back to her work in the kitchen. "And," she added, "in case no one already asked you, you're staying for supper."

"Great!" he smiled. "Thanks!" Then, speaking to Idella and Kenny, "Now, what's this about something you got today?"

"Look!" Kenny said, running to the piano. "And I can play it, too!"

"Just *pretend*, you mean," said Idella. "I can make noise like that. But you can't play like Uncle Charles."

"You play something, Uncle Charles," Kenny said.

"Sure. Just slide over a little. Now," he said, as he sat down beside Kenny, "let's have us a little 'happy' music."

He began to play at first with just his left hand. Then his right hand started

playing, too, and with both hands together he played some fine, lively music. He was making it up as he went along. It sounded so nice to hear some real music instead of just a lot of noise!

Uncle Charles played some more and some more and some more and it was all very pretty.

"I have an idea that might be fun," he said to Kenny. "We'll both play."

Kenny was embarrassed. "I can't really play," he said.

192

"Yes you can," his uncle said, "and I'm not jivin'." He showed Kenny where to put his fingers to play a simple three-note chord. "Now, I'll start a little tune over here and whenever I stop, that's when you come in over there with your chord. Ready?"

"Ready."

Uncle Charles played some more music he made up as he went along. Every time he stopped and nodded his head, Kenny would play the chord he had learned. That gave his uncle's playing a livelier sound.

"Dance with me, Daddy," Idella said. So her father swooped her up. Around and around and around the room they danced with much foolishness.

By now, Kenny was giggling so much he could hardly play.

"But the neighbors! The neighbors!"

said his mother, quite worried. "It's fine having music but we can't raise the roof."

And, sure enough, the doorbell rang, just as his mother had feared, and some of the neighbors from upstairs and downstairs were there.

But they were not angry at all—they were happy and came dancing in to the music! It was great to see so many people having a good time.

When Uncle Charles and Kenny finished playing, they both smiled and bowed to the neighbors, who clapped their hands and said thank you. Then the neighbors danced right out the door again even though the music had already stopped!

"See, Kenny?" said his uncle. "You *can* play."

"Maybe I'll be the best some day," Kenny said, very pleased.

"Well, I wouldn't worry about being the best. The main thing is that you like to make music."

Kenny's mother came in the room saying that supper was almost ready. "And," she said, "I was just talking on the telephone to Gramma and she's coming over later to see how you're doing with the piano."

"Now," said Kenny's father, smiling, "if you two musicians will get back to work, my lady friend and I can dance a little more before supper. That piano found a happy home, all right."

Working with Root Words

You know that an ending added to a root word is called a *suffix*. Name the root and the suffix in each of these words:

movement   information   quietness

statement   operation   thickness

A syllable that is added in front of a root is called a *prefix*. A prefix changes the meaning of a root. How does the prefix *un-* change the meanings of these words?

unsafe   undress   unfair

unsure   uneven   unbutton

In all these words, adding the prefix *un-* changes the meaning of the root word to its opposite. *Unsafe* means the opposite of *safe*. *Undress* means "to take off clothes," the opposite of "to dress."

Another prefix which makes the root word mean the opposite is *dis-*. "Ted likes school, but Jeff *dislikes* it." If your mother

is *displeased*, how does she feel? When snow *disappears*, what happens to it?

Re- is a prefix that sometimes means "again." If you *reopen* a box, you open it again. *Re-* also means "back." That is the meaning it adds to *turn* in *return*. If you *recover* your lost money, you get it back. When you *recover* from being sick, you get back to the way you usually feel.

Some prefixes, like *un-*, have very clear meanings. Other prefixes, like *re-*, don't have a clear or exact meaning in all the words that use them. For example, *remove* is made up of *re-* and *move*, but when you *remove* your books from the desk, you are not moving them "back" or "again."

In the word *mischief* there is a prefix, *mis-*. We don't usually think of the meaning of the prefix and root in *mischief*, though. In other words with *mis-*, the meaning of "wrong" or "bad" is added. What does "misunderstand the directions" mean?

Don't worry about the *exact* meaning of prefixes and suffixes every time. Let prefixes, suffixes, and roots help you to attack long words. Usually the other words in a sentence will help you to figure out the meaning.

A prefix is always a syllable. When you break a word into syllables, a "strange" word often turns out to be familiar. Look at this word—*unknown*. It may look strange at first. But if you remove the prefix, you find the familiar word *known*.

Try This

The questions below can be answered "yes" or "no." To answer them you will have to recognize root words. Be ready to tell why your answer is "yes" or "no." You will have to tell how you figured out some unfamiliar words.

1. If Miss White has misplaced your paper, can you take it home?
2. If you make an unimportant mistake, is it serious?

3. When friends disagree, do they get along with each other?
4. Do you usually dislike a thoughtless boy?
5. If shoes are uncomfortable, do you dislike wearing them?
6. If you are undecided, have you made up your mind?

Many words have both a prefix and a suffix. *Unbelievable* is such a word. Can you tell what it means in this sentence? "The riches of the king's castle were unbelievable."

Some words have more than one prefix. *Undiscovered* is such a word. What are the two prefixes? Does *undiscovered* also have a suffix?

You can see why it is important to know about prefixes and suffixes. If you know one root word, you probably know a whole family of related words. See how easy it is to read and understand the words that are related to *notice*.

The mistake went *unnoticed*.

That is a *noticeable* spot on your shirt.

Mrs. Green was *noticeably* upset by the news.

Try This

You can build word families by adding prefixes and suffixes to the root words below. On a paper write the words you make. Then use each word in a sentence that makes sense.

1. *cover*. Try the prefixes *re-*, *un-*, *dis-*. Can you add *-y* to one of these words? Try *-ing* and *-able*.
2. *move*. Add *un-* and *-able*. Can you add any other suffixes to *move*?
3. *place*. Add *re-* and *-able*. Then try *re-* and *-ment*. Can you think of other words that have this root?

What Did You Learn?

1. Is a syllable a prefix? Is a prefix a syllable?
2. Sometimes — but not always — a prefix or suffix helps you to understand the meaning of a word. What else helps?

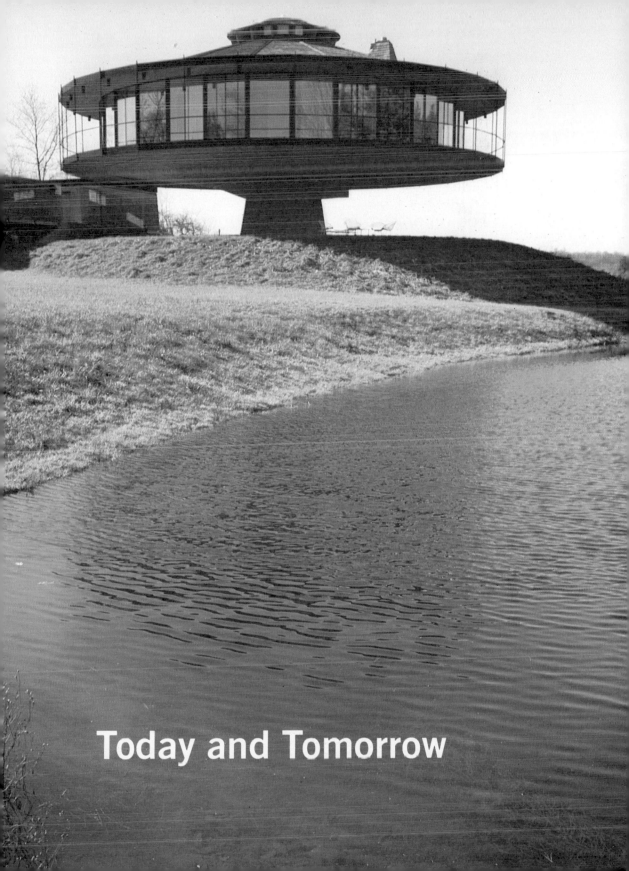

Today and Tomorrow

Our Push-Button World

Today more than ever before our work is being done by machines.

Can you believe that robots are working for us?

Can you believe that a machine can do thousands of problems in a second?

Can you believe that food can be cooked in a cold oven?

Some of these things may seem like magic, but they are all real. They are all happening in our push-button world.

Robots

You may think that all robots are those scary things you see on TV that look like men and move like machines. But a robot can be any kind of machine that works more or less by itself. All it needs is someone to push the right button.

202

Think about what happens when you ride in an elevator. You step in and push a button. The door shuts, and the elevator goes up or down. It stops where you told it

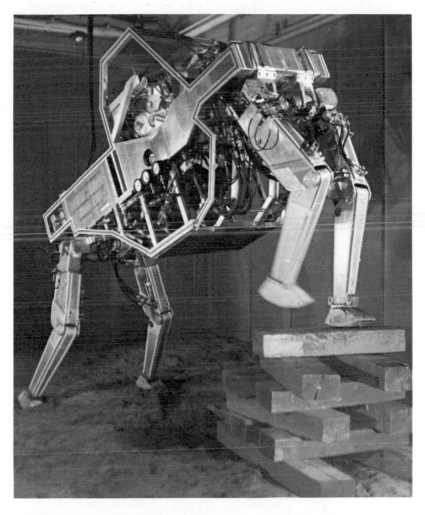

This robot has four legs. What things do you think it can do?

Look — no hands!
This robot works
when you step on
the mat.

204

to stop when you pushed the button. Then the door opens. No one has to run this kind of elevator. It is a kind of robot.

When you step in front of the doors of a big market, they open. No one opens them for you. You go into the market, and the doors shut. Your step on a mat in front of the doors made them open. Or you made them open by getting in the path of a beam of light from an electric eye. Either way, it was a kind of robot that worked the doors.

You can put in a coin, push a button, and a machine will do the washing. You do not even have to stay around to watch. Water runs in and out, things splash around, lights go on and off. At last, the washing spins dry, and you can take it out of the machine. The washing is done, step by step, by a kind of robot.

All robots are machines, but not all machines are robots. To be a real robot, a machine must go from one step to the next by itself. Each step seems to push a button for the step that comes next. This is what happens when a stack of records is played on a record player. Once the stack of records has been put on, all you have to do is turn on the machine. The records are played, one by one, and at the end of the last record, the machine turns itself off. The record player is a kind of robot.

These boxlike machines are computers. They help men think and plan.

Computers

Today, there is so much work to be done that people alone cannot do it all. Even with different kinds of robot machines, people need more help. They need help in thinking. As wonderful as men's brains are, they cannot do all the thinking and planning that must be done. Men need the kind of help they can get from computers.

The computers you see in the picture do not look as important as they are. They look like desks and boxes, but don't let this fool you. Like your head, a computer has its most important parts on the inside.

Computers are sometimes called thinking machines. This may not be a bad name for them. A computer can do some of the same things a man's brain can do.

A computer can store bits of information, and it can give out bits of information. So can a brain.

A computer can do hard problems. So can a brain.

In some ways a computer works better

than a brain. In other ways it doesn't work as well. A computer can be much faster than the best brain in the world. But a brain can store thousands of times as many bits of information.

We may call a computer a thinking machine, but it does not really think as a man thinks. A man can think with many kinds of big and small ideas. A computer can use only the bits of information that have been fed into it. A computer is made

Computers can help children
with their school work.

by people, is used by people, and cannot work without people. It cannot think for itself.

Today, we are using computers to do many kinds of work. Computers are printing newspapers and books. They are writing checks and making out bills. Computers are running ships, planes, and factories. They are planning cities and teaching children in schools.

Without computers we could not go into space. Computers send up rockets, tell astronauts what to do in space, take pictures, and help with landings. Without computers, men could not land on the moon and come back to earth.

New Machines in the Kitchen

Where do you go for a drink of cold water? What do you have to do to get a hot drink?

In the kitchen of tomorrow, you may have a small machine for drinks which is run by a computer. From this one small drink machine you will get many different kinds of hot or cold drinks. You can have your drink with or without sugar and milk. All you will have to do is to put down a cup or glass and push a button to get the drink you want — the way you want it.

You may have an oven that cooks without getting hot. Food in the oven is baked by microwaves. Microwaves do not heat the oven or the air in the oven. Only the inside of the food is heated. Let's see what happens when a big potato is baked in a microwave oven.

The potato is put in, and a dial is set for four minutes. The oven door is shut, and a button is pushed. Microwaves, which cannot be seen, bounce this way and that way inside the oven. The waves go in and out of the potato and cook it from the inside. In less than a minute, you can smell the potato baking. In four minutes, a bell rings. The potato is all baked. The potato is hot, but the oven is cold.

Microwaves heat only the food. The food

In kitchens of tomorrow,
work can be done faster and more easily.

can be baked on an ordinary glass dish or plate. It can even be cooked on a sheet of paper and the paper will not burn! The food cooks fast, and nothing else gets hot.

Yes, things are changing in our push-button world. New machines are changing our ways of living and working.

Moving Around

It is hard to move around today. It is hard to get from one place to another in most cities. It is getting harder all the time.

Cities are growing very fast. What will happen when our cities are far bigger than they are today?

There will be more people and more cars. There will be more people trying to get to the same places at the same time. Will we have one great, big traffic jam? Or will we have new and better ways of getting from one place to another?

One of our big-city problems is that too much space is taken up by freeways, streets, and parking lots. Some of the people now making plans for the cities of tomorrow hope to put all cars underground. This would make the city more pleasant for people.

One problem in cities is too many cars.

Electric Cars and Computers

Some planners also hope that all cars, trucks, and buses will be electric. Electric cars will not make our air dirty, the way our cars do today. And they will make very little noise as they move along.

Some people think that each electric car will have a small computer in its trunk.

The driver will push a few buttons, and the computer will do the rest.

Roads, too, may have computers. Each highway will have electric wires built into the road bed. Computers will then control all the traffic that moves on the road.

Imagine what it may be like then to ride

Electric cars, like this one, will not make our air dirty.

across the city. Your electric car will move itself onto a freeway under the control of a computer. It will speed along as fast as a hundred miles an hour. No one will have to drive. All you will do is push a button to tell the computer how far you want to go. Then you can sit back and read. Or you can look out at other cars that are also moving along under computer control.

On a computer highway, four times as many cars will travel faster and with far less danger than on a road of today. There will be little danger of one car bumping into another, and so all cars can move along at high speed.

New Kinds of Trains

On long trips across the country, people may be traveling in new ways. Some of the new ways of traveling on land will not need wheels. Air will take the place of wheels. New kinds of trains will move just above the ground. They will be held up by a cushion of air.

This air train has no wheels.
It moves above the ground on a cushion of air.

The picture shows an air train in France. It glides just above its rail, which looks like a low wall. The air train speeds along on a very thin cushion of air. The air is pushed downward by fans, and the train is pulled ahead by a giant propeller. It is said that this air train goes as fast as 250 miles an hour.

216

Tube trains are now being planned to go even faster. Air from in front of the train will be pushed around the sides of the train to the back. Jets of air will shoot out the back, and the train will rocket ahead. Riding on a cushion of air, it will shoot across the country at a speed of 600 miles an hour!

New Planes

Before long, there will be new planes bigger than any we now have. Giant jets that seat 1000 people may someday be speeding across the sky many times faster than the planes of today. In about two hours, one of the giant jets will fly all the way across the country from California to New York.

These giant jets will be used only for long air trips. Helicopters and other smaller planes will be used for shorter trips.

One new kind of smaller plane doesn't

Straight up, straight down plane.
It doesn't need a long runway for take-off or landing.

need a long runway for take-off. It goes
straight up from the ground into the air.
Its four propellers are in tubes that turn
this way and that way as needed. Because
of the way the propellers work, this plane
can do many of the things helicopters do.
It can take-off and land in a small space.
And it can hover—stay in one place in the

218

This hovercraft moves just above the water.
It can move over land, too.

air — just as helicopters do. But when this plane flies, it is two times as fast as a fast helicopter.

Water Craft

One of the new ways of water travel is by hovercraft. This strange craft moves *over* water, not on it or in it. It rides on a cushion of air that keeps the boat above the water.

The hovercraft is not an ordinary boat. It has a flat bottom and a kind of skirt made of rubber. A giant fan pushes air from the top of the craft down inside the rubber skirt. This makes the boat hover over the waves. Propellers speed the hovercraft along on its cushion of air.

This is a hydrofoil, speeding over the water.

An important thing about the hovercraft is that it can come out of the water and move over land. It can hover over land just as it hovers over water. But it cannot climb any steep hills.

The hydrofoil is another strange craft. It seems to be part boat and part plane. Hydrofoils are not new. But new, fast kinds of hydrofoils are now being made. You may have had a ride in one across a bay, a river, or a lake.

When a hydrofoil gets going, it lifts itself up. As the craft speeds up, only part of it stays in the water. When you ride in a hydrofoil, all you can see is flying spray as the craft speeds over the water.

There are other new ways of moving from place to place—by land, sea, and air. Many new ways are being planned, tested, and tried out. You read about them in newspapers and see them on TV. We need better ways to travel. We will have them as fast as people are willing to change from old ways to new.

Keeping in Touch

No matter where we live, most of us need to communicate, or keep in touch, with people who live somewhere else. How do we do it?

We go to see people.

We write letters and send them by mail.

We call people on the telephone.

Most people communicate with friends and family in all three ways. And, as time goes on, we are making more and more telephone calls.

Telephones are not new. They have been around for about a hundred years. But new kinds of telephones are coming out all the time.

Most telephones today have dials. But a new kind has push buttons, which work faster than a dial. Just push the buttons for the number you want, and the call is made at once.

Another is the picture phone. With two

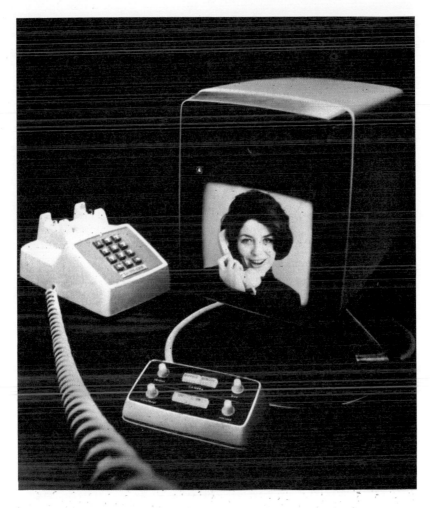

With this push-button picture phone,
you can see the person you are talking to.

picture phones, people can see each other
as they talk. But if someone with a picture
phone does not want to be seen, he can push
a button. This will shut off his picture.

Television

In the summer of 1969, millions of people in many parts of the world watched the same thing at the same time. This had never happened before.

How could people in so many different places see the same thing? And what was so important that millions of people wanted to watch?

As you may have guessed, the people were seeing the first two men land and walk on the moon. Sitting in front of their television sets, people could see and hear what was happening far off in space. They could see the President of the United States speak to the astronauts from his office. Imagine being able to say "Congratulations!" to someone on the moon!

Have you ever wondered how television programs get to your set? How do pictures and sounds get to you from around the world, and even from out in space?

Television signals are sent out as waves,

called *microwaves*. Microwaves travel in a straight line. So, when television signals go out, they soon hit the Earth, or they go off into space. Help is needed if the signals are to travel *around* the Earth for more than twenty or thirty miles.

There are several ways of getting television signals from where a program is made to your set many miles away.

One way is by cable. Cables can carry

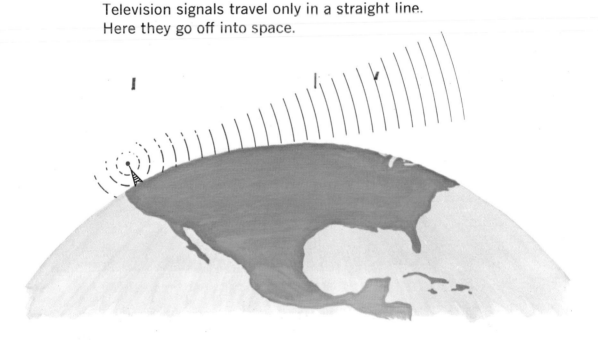

Television signals travel only in a straight line. Here they go off into space.

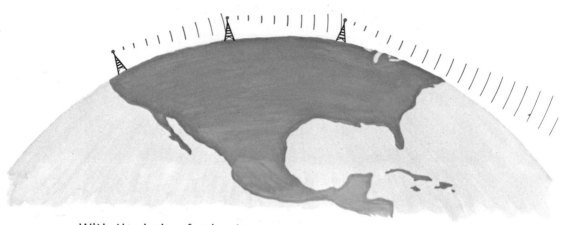

With the help of relay towers,
television signals go from place to place on the earth.

signals through mountains, over cities, and along the bottom of the sea.

Another way of sending television signals is by relay. The microwaves go first to a relay tower not far away. They are sent from there to the next relay tower, and then on to another. This goes on, from one relay tower to the next, for many miles. At each tower, the television signals are made stronger and then sent out.

But relay towers cannot be used for

226

sending signals across oceans. For this, something else is needed.

Satellites

Satellites in space are a bit like relay towers. But satellites in space can relay programs around the world. Television signals can go out from a spot on the Earth to a communication satellite in space. The satellite can then send the signals to another spot on the Earth, far from the starting place.

Telstar was the first communication satellite to relay television programs to us from lands across the sea. This was in 1962. We now have many communication satellites around the Earth.

Satellites are sometimes called our eyes in space. They are used in many ways to get and send information we need. Echo, Early Bird, and Telstar are the names of some of the first satellites used for communication. A communication satellite is called *comsat*, for short.

227

This is Telstar, a communication satellite.

Comsats are now used for telephone calls to far places as well as for relaying television signals. They can be fitted with equipment which allows us to communicate with men in space, or to help planes fly over the sea. They are also used in making maps. An "eye" in space can see a large part of the Earth at one time. It can send back its

Men keep in touch with satellites in space.

information, and good new maps can be made.

Weather satellites collect information too. They move far above land and sea, sending back pictures of clouds. They have other ways too of keeping track of the weather. When all the information collected by weather satellites is received on Earth, we can tell whether a heavy rain is on the way or whether tomorrow will be hot and sunny.

In time to come, comsats may be used in many more ways than they are today. Some satellites might tape all television programs and store them. Then people could watch a program from any country. They could see again a program from last year, or the year before.

Satellites might also be used to help animals. The eyes in space could keep track of the wild animals on land, the fish in the sea, and the birds in the air. The information we received would help us to study the animals' ways. Then it might be possible to help them find food and a safe place to feed.

How wonderful it will be if satellites can help all the living things of our planet keep in touch with each other!

This craft has TV and other equipment
for exploring under the sea.

Exploring the Sea

Some men always want to find out more
about their world. They are the men who
explore, looking for new places to live and
new ways of living.

Men have explored this planet from east
to west, from the ice fields of the north to
the ice fields of the south. It may seem that
there are no more places on the Earth to
explore. But this is not so.

Men still know very little about the ocean.
When we hear the word *ocean*, we think of
water. But there is far more to the ocean
than water. What is underneath the water?

The Ocean Floor

Land under the ocean is not too different from land on other parts of the Earth. There are bumps and cracks — mountains and low spots. The land is covered with rocks, sand, mud, clay, and soil. Different parts of the ocean are called by different names. But there is just one great big ocean. As far as we know, Earth is the only planet that has an ocean.

In some ways, it may be as important to explore the sea as to explore outer space. We may find in the sea many things that we need.

Underwater Explorers

It is not easy to explore the bottom of the ocean. One way to do it is to go down in one of the strange craft used for underwater exploring. One kind is a big ball with walls of thick, strong metal. It has thick, strong windows for underwater cameras.

Another kind of craft is made to move in

With windows on all sides,
explorers can get a good look underwater.

This craft is called FLIP.
FLIP is 355 feet long.

water, to dive, and to skim along on the ocean floor, using its cameras to explore.

A most strange and funny-looking craft is called FLIP. On top of the water, it looks like a kind of boat. It is long, and very slim at one end. The slim end can be filled with water in less then twelve minutes. When the water is in, FLIP flips! The slim end tilts down and sinks, sticking into the bottom. The other end, as high as a four-story building, sticks up in the air. This end is where the sea explorers live. Sometimes FLIP stands this way for ten

234

FLIP flips. Its slim end goes down
and sticks into the ocean floor.

days at a time, and its divers explore the sea.

You may know someone who swims and dives in underwater gear. With an air pack on his back, the diver can stay under for a time. The fins help him to swim like a fish. But even with his back pack, he cannot take air from the water as fish do. He must come up, out of the water, before the air in his pack is all used up.

Some divers work underwater for days at a time without coming up. They live in a kind of undersea building called *Sealab*. Teams of divers eat, sleep, and work in

Men from Sealab work underwater.

Sealab. They go in and out of Sealab's open hatch several hundred feet underwater.

Sealab divers have explored ocean water and kept track of the fish. They have also made maps of the ocean floor.

In the world of tomorrow, some men will work even farther down, in the deeper, darker parts of the ocean. For this, they may use a craft like *Deep Diver*. This is a work boat that can carry four men down to the bottom. It can stay down, and the workers can go in and out of the craft as they work on the ocean floor.

Exploring may also be done by robot submarines, run by computers. Small submarines and machines with robot arms will move about, dig, and do many kinds of work deep down in the sea.

What Explorers Look For

With all the diving and exploring going on, what are men looking for? What do men hope to find in the undersea world?

First of all, they hope to get food. There

are millions of people who do not get enough to eat. More food and more kinds of food have to be found to feed the hungry. Explorers are looking at some of the strange plants and animals as possible food for man.

In time, there may be great sea farms where green plants grow and are cared for by people. The plants will be picked and used for food. There may be great sea ranches too. On the ranches, fish and other sea animals will be cared for.

Power is another thing that explorers are looking for. They hope to find ways to use the power of the ocean. There is great power in the waves and tides and in the deep rivers that run along the bottom of the ocean.

Sea explorers are also looking for minerals. Oil and gas are under the ocean floor. Metals and other kinds of minerals are in and underneath the sea floor.

Today we have undersea oil wells. But it still takes too much money to dig minerals from the ocean floor or get them out of the water. In time, men will find cheaper ways of capturing the riches of the sea. Then we will get from the ocean the things we need to live on land.

This animal may be of help on sea farms.
Here, one is being trained to herd fish.

Apartment House

A filing-cabinet of human lives
Where people swarm like bees in tunneled
  hives,
Each to his own cell in the towered comb,
Identical and cramped—we call it home.

GERALD RAFTERY

Jets

Listen—listen
The planes go over!
(Silent the bees
In the clouds of clover.)
Faster than sound,
Miles in the sky
Like bees about heaven
The bright jets fly.
All the world's power
Come out from cover
Listen—listen
The planes go over.

IRENE GOUGH

Cities of Tomorrow

Important changes are taking place in our cities and towns. Our cities are growing fast to take care of all the people. Old buildings are coming down. New buildings are going up. Small cities are growing into big cities. Big cities are growing into bigger cities.

In time, many of our old cities will be all made over. But we will need more than the old, made-over cities to take care of all the people of tomorrow. We will need many new cities too.

Where will the new cities of tomorrow be? Will there be some on the moon? Will there be some on other planets? Will there be some on the bottom of the sea?

Most people think that our new cities will be right here on Earth. Some will be near the old cities. Others will be built on land that is not now being used.   Streets and buildings will spread out on land that is not much good for anything else.

What will it be like to live in one of the

Tomorrow City may look something like this.

242

planned cities of tomorrow? Will they be better than the cities of today? Let us jump ahead a number of years. Let us visit *Tomorrow City* and find out what it is like.

What is happening underground?

Downtown in Tomorrow City

When you go downtown in Tomorrow City, you may drive your electric car on a computer freeway. In Tomorrow City, all the freeways and roads are underground. You will drive on the freeway that is just for cars. There are other freeways for trucks and buses.

At the end of your freeway trip, you will push a button in your car. Then it will park itself in a big underground parking building.

But to get downtown, you may not wish to drive your own car. You may then go on one of the fast underground trains that moves on a cushion of air. When you come to your stop, you can get off the train and go the rest of the way in one of the little cars that moves on tracks. These little cars are called people pods. Each one has seats for two to four people.

To ride in a people pod, you first buy a ticket from a computer. You push buttons on the computer to tell it where you want to

244

go. You put the ticket in a slot in the small computer on the people pod. The computer then controls your ride along tracks under the city.

When you get out of the people pod, or out of the parking building, you go up to the street. You move up on an escalator. Then, if you wish, you may climb into a *mini-bus* that runs from building to building. Or you may stand on a moving sidewalk that will take you where you want to go.

Downtown in Tomorrow City is a place that people enjoy. There are trees, pleasant gardens, and wide walkways. The only cars moving about are the mini-buses, which make very little noise, even in rush hours. There is no honking of horns. There are none of the sounds or smells of cars and trucks. The air is clean and you can see the bright blue sky above the tall buildings.

New Buildings

Some of Tomorrow City's buildings are different from those in cities of today.

245

Some are just bigger and taller. There are many highrise buildings made of metal and glass.

Some buildings have strange new shapes. Some are tall and round, like giant towers. Tubes for people to walk and ride in run from one tower building to the next. Some buildings are shaped like domes. Some are big balls with glass on the outside.

There are many buildings that are up, off

Push a button and this house
moves slowly around in a full circle.

the ground. They look like buildings on legs. Under these buildings there are gardens, walks, and places where people can sit and rest.

Some of the buildings seem to have been made of children's blocks. Hundreds of giant blocks are stacked, one on top of another. Some stick out, this way and that. Each of the blocks is an apartment for a family to live in.

Boxlike apartments are piled together this way and that way.

This building goes up fast with the help
of a Skycrane helicopter.

In Tomorrow City, some apartment
buildings are built by putting ready-made
apartments together. Each apartment is
made in a factory miles away from the city.

Each apartment is like a big, odd-shaped
box. It has rooms with windows, doors,

248

floors, and walls. There are rugs on the floors, and there is paper on the walls. One room is a kitchen, with built-in sink, dishwasher, ovens, and other things needed in a kitchen.

The box-like apartments are moved to the city from the factories where they are made. Then they are picked up and put in place by giant helicopters and cranes. As soon as the apartments are fitted together, families can move in.

An apartment in Tomorrow City.

At Home in Tomorrow City

Today, fathers and mothers who work usually go away from home each day. But in a city of tomorrow, many people work right at home. One room in the home is a work place. It has in it computers, TV sets, robot machines, and picture phones. A

Children will have new things to play on in Tomorrow City.

worker can sit all day and work by pushing buttons.

If you live in Tomorrow City, you can do your shopping, too, without going out. You first call a store by pushing buttons on your picture phone. Then, from the picture phone at the store, you see some of the things you are interested in buying. You push buttons to show what you want to order. You pay by putting a card with your number on it into a slot in your phone. A computer at the store "reads" the number, makes out a bill, and mails it to you.

The big apartment buildings in Tomorrow City have large playgrounds for children. Some have school rooms too. Many children go to school in the same building in which they live.

As cities grow, they must be carefully planned to take care of the problems we have today. With careful planning, Tomorrow City will be a better place for all the people who live there.

Picture in Your Mind

On television you see things happening before your eyes. You may see astronauts landing on the moon or a fishing boat putting out to sea. You can see how people live in many different countries. You can watch cowboys driving their herds across the plains and children flying kites in Japan.

Stories on television are told with pictures as well as words. In fact, words are not so important on television as they are in books. It is so easy to enjoy stories on television that you may wonder why people still like to read stories in books.

There are many reasons. One is that libraries have more great stories for you to choose from than you can ever see on television. You can choose a story at any time to go with the way you feel. On television other people always choose for you.

Another reason why people often choose

books instead of television is that you can read a book almost anywhere without bothering other people.

You can learn many things from watching television. But if you want information on some topic, it is better to go to a library than a TV set.

Can you think of any other reasons for choosing books instead of television — at least some of the time?

Reading with Pictures

The stories you read are more enjoyable if you can picture what is happening, just as television does. From the words you read, you should get an idea of what the people in a story look like, how they dress and act, where they live, and what is happening to them. Of course, writers don't tell you everything. But they tell you enough so that you can imagine the rest.

Look at this picture. You know it is a man even though the artist made only a few lines. Your imagination made you see a

253

whole man.   Your imagination can work the same way when you are reading.

Try This

As you read the following paragraphs, try to see what is happening.   Use what the writer tells you, but add anything that fits the picture.   Imagine colors and shapes, too.

(A) Kathy was watching the street from her living room window.   Rain was streaming down the window pane.   It was too wet to go outside, and there was nothing for Kathy to do inside the small apartment.   Her brother and his friend Joe were playing checkers on the little table in front of the sofa.   Her mother was in the kitchen getting supper.

(B) On the street below the traffic was heavy.   On the sidewalk people hurried by each other, many carrying bright-colored umbrellas.   It was wet and windy and getting dark.   Kathy watched a yellow taxi pull over in front of the apartment house. Someone inside was paying the driver.

Then the door opened and out came a red umbrella. All Kathy could see were red storm boots and the bottom of a yellow raincoat. Suddenly the wind turned the umbrella inside out. Then Kathy recognized her cousin Pam hurrying to the door. Soon the buzzer would ring.

To help you tell about the picture you imagined, here are some questions. Not everyone will answer the questions in the same way. Talk over your answers with other boys and girls. Try to figure out why some answers are different.

What did you see in the living room besides the children? Could you see the color of the sofa? How old were the children? How were they dressed? Were there lights on the street and on the cars? What colors did you see? How old was Pam?

In many different kinds of reading it is important to try to see what the words tell you. You may be reading directions. It is a good idea to picture in your mind what the directions say before you try to follow them. Here are directions for making a toy horse. On the page are three pictures of toy horses. Which one fits Paragraph C?

(C) Use a big cork for the body of the horse. Push toothpicks into the cork to make legs. Use a small cork for the head. Put it on one end of a small stick. Put the other end of this stick in the body. This stick is the neck. Wrap bright yarn around the neck and tie it for the mane. Make a matching yarn tail. Pin black beads onto the small cork for eyes. Cut a saddle from paper and paste it on the big cork. Make small paper ears.

What Did You Learn?

1. In what ways are reading and watching television alike?
2. Should you expect the pictures you imagine while reading to be just like other people's?
3. When you read, why should you try to picture what the words say?

THE HORSE WHO HAD HIS PICTURE IN THE PAPER

BY PHYLLIS McGINLEY
PICTURES BY HELEN STONE

There is a city called New York, so
crowded with tall buildings that you must
tilt back your head and look straight up to
see the sky. So, of course, there isn't
room for green fields or fat red barns.

Nearly everybody lives upstairs — even the horses.

In one of the buildings lived a horse named Jocy. Joey was a contented horse. He liked his upstairs stable and he liked his stall, which was sunny, with a window to look out of.

He liked working for Mr. Polaski who sold fruit and vegetables to city folk. He liked the people he met as he pulled his cart about the city streets. And he was fond of his friend, the Percheron, who lived in the left-hand stall. In fact, he was contented as a horse can be, until the day that Brownie moved into the right-hand stall next door to his.

Brownie was a Police Horse, and he never let anyone forget it. He was shining brown all over except for his mane and his tail, which were black. And he was very proud. He was proud of his mane and proud of his tail and proud of being on the Force. And he was very, *very* proud because he had had his picture in the paper.

He treated the other horses coolly because they were ordinary fellows who pulled carts, like Joey, or great wagons, like the Percheron. He, himself, carried a Police Sergeant on his back and was much admired by people on the street.

Sometimes he led parades up Fifth Avenue and sometimes he kept the crowds in order when something exciting was going on. And he had been to school to learn how to jump over bars and how not to be afraid of loud noises, and how to act like a policeman.

"It isn't just any horse who gets on the Force," he boasted to Joey. "We're picked for our brains, you know. Besides, I'm a hero. That's why I had my picture in the paper."

"Is that good?" asked Joey.

"Of course it's good," said Brownie. "It got my Sergeant a promotion. So now he has more money in the bank and I have more apples with my lunch."

Joey didn't care about the apples. Mr.

Polaski gave him all the apples he wanted, anyhow. But he knew that Mr. Polaski had six children at home who were always needing new shoes, and that sometimes he was worried about money. "A vegetable cart is no gold mine," Joey often heard him say.

Now Joey wished he could have *his* picture in the paper. Maybe then Mr. Polaski would get a promotion, too.

He thought and he thought, but he couldn't decide how to go about it.

"How do you get to be a hero?" he asked Brownie shyly.

"Save a man's life, like me," answered Brownie.

"Did you rescue him from a burning building?" asked Joey.

"Not at all," Brownie snorted. "I saved his life by not stepping on him. When a crowd pushed him, he fell under my feet. And I stood still as a statue. It's the way they taught me in school."

He looked so pleased with himself that

Joey decided just standing still must be quite difficult for a Police Horse.

But the Percheron nearly choked on his oats. "Think of the lives *I've* saved," he whispered to Joey. "Thousands and thousands! Why, the city is *filled* with people I haven't stepped on."

But Joey didn't laugh. He just went on wondering how he could be a hero and get his picture in the paper.

Whenever he saw a crowd he trotted toward it, hoping somebody would fall

under his feet. But Mr. Polaski always pulled him back again. And although he stood as quietly as a statue while Mr. Polaski sold his vegetables, *that* didn't make him a hero. It just brought him pats on the nose and a carrot or two.

Once a lady with a camera took his picture as he was taking a lump of sugar from the hand of a friendly little girl. Unluckily, a fly was buzzing around him and he had to swish his tail just as the lady snapped the camera. So probably it wasn't a good likeness. Anyway, he didn't hear of the picture appearing in any paper.

Then one day he thought his chance had come.

Mr. Polaski was selling a cabbage to a woman in front of an apartment house. Suddenly a little boy, just learning to walk, came down the apartment house steps ahead of his nurse, and wobbled into the street. It was a busy street, with cars zooming by and trucks rushing to reach the corner before the light turned red.

The nurse called to the little boy but he didn't stop. The lady was too busy poking the cabbage to notice him. And Mr. Polaski was too busy with the lady.

But Joey saw. And quick as a flash, he reached out and caught the little boy by the seat of his pants.

"Now I'm a hero!" he thought to himself. "And my picture will surely be in the paper."

But the little boy began to cry and the nurse came running after him, crying, "Help!" The lady dropped the cabbage and said, "I do believe your horse bit that child!"

And since Mr. Polaski hadn't been watching, he couldn't explain that Joey was only rescuing the little boy from the cars and the trucks.

Mr. Polaski had to tell the nurse he was sorry, and on the way down the street he scolded Joey as if he had done something wrong.

"A vegetable cart isn't a gold mine," he said crossly. "And now you have lost me a customer." And he didn't even give Joey an apple with his lunch.

"How am I to get my picture in the paper?" he asked the Percheron that night.

"Join a circus!" snapped the Percheron throwing a bit of hay crossly onto the floor. He was fond of Joey but he believed that Brownie was putting foolish ideas into his head.

"Join a circus," Joey said to himself, thoughtfully. "Why yes, circus horses *do* get their pictures in the paper. I

266

could learn to walk on my hind legs and do tricks."

But when he tried walking on his hind legs in the stall, he frightened the man who was bringing him his oats. And after he had tried to bow the way circus horses do, he ached so badly all over that he limped as he pulled the cart.

So he had to give up the idea of becoming a circus horse. But his hope of helping

Mr. Polaski led him into trouble one June morning.

It was a very pleasant morning. Joey was trotting along, enjoying the sunshine, while Mr. Polaski from the front seat of the cart sang out, "Strawberries! Strawberries! Nice fresh Strawberries!"

A lady called to them from the upstairs window of a house and Mr. Polaski, stopping the cart, climbed the steps to sell her two boxes of berries. He left Joey standing still as a statue.

But just as Mr. Polaski was counting his change in the hall, Joey heard a sound that made his ears stand straight up on his head. It was the exciting sound of trumpets and drums and marching feet.

"A parade," thought Joey. He knew about parades. Brownie had often told him that the horse who led one was sure to have his picture taken.

"Boom!" went the drums. "Tarara, tum-tum, tara!" tooted the horns. It was too much for Joey.

268

Lifting his feet smartly, off he trotted in the direction of the music. He reached the corner just as the marchers reached it too. The crowds watching the parade were too surprised to stop him. Even the policemen noticed him too late. Before they knew it, Joey was there at the head of the line, ready to lead the paraders up the avenue.

The only trouble was that he had taken a left turn while the parade was trying to turn to the right. There he was in the way of everybody!

The fife players stopped so suddenly that the horn players stepped on their heels. The drummers stepped on the heels of the horn players. And the men who were only marching stepped on the heels of the drummers. The whole parade came to a stop.

When Mr. Polaski ran up to the corner, the policeman was holding Joey, the crowd was laughing, and the paraders were very angry. It was a terrible moment.

Mr. Polaski explained that Joey meant

no harm. So the policeman let them go
with a warning and the parade started up
again. But Mr. Polaski seemed so
frightened and upset that Joey realized
he had made a terrible mistake.

"Whatever has got into you, Joey?" asked Mr. Polaski. "A vegetable cart is no gold mine. But you'll make me poorer than I am, if you don't behave yourself.

271

Then what will happen to my six children?"

Poor Joey! He felt very sad, especially since Brownie's Sergeant had received another promotion. Now Brownie was prouder than ever. He swished his black tail and tossed his black mane and boasted about how well he had pushed back the crowds one day when the President of the United States drove by.

He even had his picture in the newspaper again. He was leading a parade.

"I'll never be a hero or anything," Joey told the Percheron. "I'm just an ordinary city horse. It's too bad for Mr. Polaski."

"You're a good fellow, Joey," said the Percheron. "Just cheer up and get that foolishness out of your head about newspaper pictures. Do your job and everything will be all right."

So Joey tried to be cheerful and well-behaved and Mr. Polaski didn't have to scold him again.

But things weren't going too well with the vegetable cart. It was now the middle of the summer and very hot in the city. It was so hot that many of Mr. Polaski's best customers moved right into the country to be comfortable. The vegetables and the fruit wilted in the heat, and new customers would not buy them. But Mr. Polaski's six children ate just as much as ever and needed as many pairs of shoes. So Mr. Polaski's face grew longer and longer.

One morning, earlier than usual, Mr. Polaski came into the stable and took Joey out to the cart.

"We're going to New Jersey, Joey," he said as he put a hat over Joey's ears to keep off the sun. "I've heard of a place where I can get fresh vegetables cheaper than here. We'll drive over and look at them."

Joey was pleased to be having an adventure. As hot as it was, he trotted along quickly in the direction that Mr. Polaski told him was New Jersey.

He trotted for blocks and blocks, winding his way through the many cars and trucks and buses. The streets were new and exciting to him and he liked it when they came to one which ran as far as he could see, beside a river. Finally, he trotted up a sort of hill and all of a sudden found himself on a great bridge

274

reaching across the water. It might have frightened another horse but Joey wasn't frightened at all. He only slowed to a walk, the better to enjoy the sight of the river and the boats skimming busily along below him.

Mr. Polaski enjoyed it too, and they were both sorry to see the toll house at the end of the bridge coming into sight. There seemed to be a crowd gathered there, and the cars, too, were moving slowly. Joey hurried a little so he could see what was going on. In fact, he edged right in front of a slow-moving truck and the driver shouted at him. But Joey didn't mind, he was so interested.

The cart stopped at the toll house,

which had flags flying from it. And then, just as Mr. Polaski started to take out his money to pay the toll, a man with a red carnation in his button-hole stepped up to them.

He wore a silk hat and carried a bunch of flowers. Behind him came several other men, some with cameras and some with pencils and pads of paper in their hands.

"Congratulations!" said the man with the silk hat. "These flowers are for you. You have also won the fifty dollar prize. What is your name, sir?"

"Polaski," said Mr. Polaski, much surprised. "Please—I don't understand."

"We are from the Department of Bridges," the man said, "and this prize is being given to the millionth person to pass the toll house. Your cart was the millionth."

"And we're reporters," said one of the men who carried pencils and paper. "There's quite a story for our papers in this. You see, we had expected a car or

276

truck or a bus to get the prize. We didn't count on a horse and cart."

"What's your horse's name?" another reporter asked. When Mr. Polaski told him, he wrote down "Joey" on the pad of paper. Then he shook Mr. Polaski's hand and several people cheered.

It was almost as good as leading a parade. The first man put the flowers in front of the cart and handed Mr. Polaski five ten-dollar bills. Then the men with cameras crowded around and cars stopped to watch and people shouted cheerfully.

"Smile, now," said a cameraman. "And hold on to your horse. We especially want a good shot of him."

"That's quite a hat he's wearing," said another. "But he needs just one more touch. He's the hero of the day, you know."

He whispered something to the man in the silk hat. Then that gentleman took the red carnation out of his buttonhole and tucked it behind Joey's ear.

278

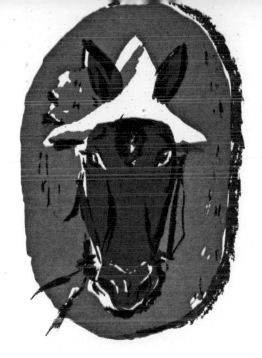

"Don't let him move," said the cameraman. But Joey wouldn't have moved for anything, not even for a hundred flies. He stood still as a statue and looked straight into the cameras. He wasn't going to take a chance on ruining *this* picture.

Afterwards the reporters patted his neck and told Mr. Polaski they admired his well-behaved horse.

"We're holding up traffic, I'm afraid," said the silk-hatted man. "You'll have to move on. But look in the papers tomorrow — you'll be sure to see yourselves."

And with everybody waving happily and the cars tooting their horns in a friendly way, Mr. Polaski and Joey moved on.

When they got back to the stable that night, Joey didn't say a word to the other horses about his adventure. Something might go wrong—perhaps the papers wouldn't use the picture after all. Besides, he was afraid his hat wasn't really becoming.

But the next morning Mr. Polaski rushed in, waving a bunch of newspapers.

"Look, Joey!" he cried. "Here we are! We're famous!" He opened one of the papers and there, almost on the front page was a picture of Joey, handsome as a circus horse, with his hat becomingly tilted, and the red carnation behind his ear. Underneath the picture it said:

NEW YORK ONLY ONE-HORSE TOWN AFTER ALL—CART-HORSE JOEY WINS FIFTY DOLLAR PRIZE

All the horses stretched their necks over their stalls to see. Even Brownie

had to take notice. "Excellent likeness,"
he had to say. And even the Percheron
said, "Well, you made it."

"But that's not all, Joey," Mr. Polaski
said. "Maybe a vegetable cart *is* a gold
mine after all. A friend of mine — he knew
me in the old country — saw that picture

first thing this morning and he telephoned me right away. He's got a farm on Long Island and he needs somebody to help him in the city. He says I'll be his partner. Every day he'll bring me his fresh vegetables and you and I will sell them. Now I won't mind if my six children grow so fast out of their shoes."

My, but Joey was happy! He said later to the Percheron, "Of course, it would have been nice to have been a real hero. But I expect this is nearly as good."

"There are all sorts of ways of being a hero," the Percheron told him kindly. "You did your job every day and didn't complain and that's as good a way as I know of. And," he added with a side glance at Brownie, still tossing his black mane in the right-hand stall, "it's certainly just as good as saving a man's life by standing still."

"Anyhow," said Joey contentedly, "I got Mr. Polaski his promotion."

Glossary

This glossary is a little dictionary. It lists some of the words found in this book. The pronunciation, which tells you how to say the word, is given in the parentheses following the word. The meaning of the word is given next.

The special symbols used to show the pronunciation are explained in the key that follows.

PRONUNCIATION KEY

a	add, map	l	look, rule	u	up, done
ā	ace, rate	m	move, seem	û(r)	urn, term
â(r)	care, air	n	nice, tin	yōo	use, few
ä	palm, father	ng	ring, song		
				v	vain, eve
b	bat, rub	o	odd, hot	w	win, away
ch	check, catch	ō	open, so	y	yet, yearn
d	dog, rod	ô	order, jaw	z	zest, muse
		oi	oil, boy	zh	vision, pleasure
e	end, pet	ou	out, now		
ē	equal, tree	ōo	pool, food	ə	the schwa,
		ŏo	took, full		an unstressed
f	fit, half				vowel representing
g	go, log	p	pit, stop		the sound spelled
h	hope, hate	r	run, poor		a in above
		s	see, pass		e in sicken
i	it, give	sh	shut, rush		i in possible
ī	ice, write	t	talk, sit		o in melon
		th	thin, both		u in circus
j	joy, ledge	th	this, bathe		
k	cool, take				

In the pronunciations an accent mark (′) is used to show which syllable of a word receives the most stress. The word *party* (pär′tē), for example, is stressed on the first syllable. Sometimes there is also a lighter accent mark (′) that shows where there is a lighter stress, as in the word *coconut* (kō′kə·nut′).

A

ache (āk) To hurt with a dull, steady pain: My feet *ache*.
ached

admire (ad·mīr′) To look upon with wonder and pleasure; to think well of: I *admire* the way she plays the piano.
admired

affect (ə·fekt′) To act upon in a way that makes some difference or change: Rain will *affect* my plans to go to the beach.

appear (ə·pir′) **1.** To come into sight: A bird *appeared* in the sky. **2.** To come before a group of people: He *appeared* in the play. **3.** To come before the judge in a court of law: He was told to *appear* in court.

B

belongings (bi·lông′ingz) The things a person owns.

bowsprit (bou′sprit′) A long pole coming from the forward part of a boat.

A bowsprit

brave (brāv) **1.** Not afraid. **2.** An Indian warrior of North America.

broth (brôth) A soup made by boiling meat, vegetables, and so on, in water.

C

cable (kā′bəl) An electric wire or group of wires, covered in a special way, used to carry telephone and telegraph messages under the ground or under the ocean.

cargo (kär′gō) Goods, or a load, carried by ship, plane, train, or truck. **cargoes**

carnation (kär·nā′shən) A white, yellow, red, or pink flower with a strong, spicy smell.

carve (kärv) **1.** To make by cutting from something, such as stone or wood: He *carved* a face in stone. **2.** To cut up, as a piece of cooked meat.
carved, carving

carving (kär′ving) **1.** The act of a person who carves. **2.** A carved figure.

case¹ (kās) **1.** A particular situation or example. **2.** The facts as they are: He studied the *case* to see who was right. **3.** An action or lawsuit in a court.

case² (kās) A box, bag, or other holder for carrying or keeping things in: a glove *case*; a pillow*case*.

cheap (chēp) Not costing much money: This hat is *cheap.*

chief (chēf) The leader of a particular group: He is *chief* of the firemen.

clearing (klir′ing) A place in the woods or forest that is free of trees.

coat of arms A design, used as the sign of a family or nation.

Coat of arms

coconut (kō′kə·nut′) The large fruit of the coconut palm with a hard shell, white meat, and a center filled with a sweet liquid.

communicate (kə·myōō′nə·kāt) To give or exchange thoughts, information, or messages.

communication (kə·myōō′nə·kā′shən) The giving or exchange of ideas, information, or messages: All our *communication* was by mail.

contented (kən·ten′tid) Happy enough with what one has or with things the way they are: He is *contented* with his new home. **contentedly**

copra (cop′rə) The dried part of the coconut that can be eaten.

coral reef (kôr′əl rēf) A stone-like shelf made from many skeletons of tiny sea animals.

count[1] (kount) **1.** To list or call off numbers in a regular order: He *counted* to 100. **2.** To add up; to find out how many: He *counted* the pencils.

count[2] (kount) In some European countries, a man of high place or position.

countdown (kount′doun′) A downward counting of the time left before something is to begin: The *countdown* began: 10 . . . 9 . . . 8 . . . 7.

counter (koun′tər) A long board or table in a restaurant, store, and so on, for eating meals or selling goods.

craft (kraft) **1.** Work calling for special skill with the hands: Making pottery and blowing glass are *crafts.* **2.** A boat, ship, airplane, and so on.

---

add, āce, câre, pälm; end, ēqual; it, īce; odd, ōpen, ôrder; tŏŏk, pōōl; up, bûrn; ə = a in *above,* e in *sicken,* i in *possible,* o in *melon,* u in *circus;* yōō — u in *fuse;* oil; pout

crane (krān) **1.** A wading bird with long legs. **2.** A machine with a long, movable arm, used to lift and move heavy objects.

A crane

crop (krop) Any plant, grown on a farm, for eating or other use: The corn *crop* is good this year.

D

deck (dek) **1.** The top platform on a ship. **2.** To dress up or decorate: The room was *decked* with flowers.

department (di·pärt′mənt) A separate section or part, as of a business, government, school, and so forth.

detective (di·tek′tiv) A person whose work is to find out hidden information.

diary (dī′ə·rē) A record kept by a person of what happens and what he thinks each day.

dome (dōm) A round roof shaped somewhat like an upside-down cup.

A dome

E

egret (ē′grit) A bird with long, white feathers and a long neck, bill, and legs.

An egret, about 2 feet high

equipment (i·kwip′mənt) A thing or things needed for some special use or purpose: Jim looked for his football *equipment*.

exclaim (iks·klām') To cry out suddenly or speak strongly, as in surprise or anger: "The supper's burning!" she *exclaimed.*

F

fife (fīf) A small flute having a shrill tone.

A fife

folk (fōk) People: The young *folk* sang songs.

fond (fond) Loving. — **fond of** Having a liking for or love of: He is *fond* of cats.

fortune (fôr'chən) 1. That which will happen in a person's future: He told her *fortune.* 2. Luck or chance, whether good or bad: He met with good *fortune.* 3. Good luck; success. 4. Much money; wealth.

freeway (frē'wā') A highway for fast travel.

frost (frôst) Weather cold enough to freeze things.

G

gather (gath'ər) 1. To bring together or come together: They *gathered* around the speaker. 2. To pick or harvest: They *gathered* the crops.

glance (glans) 1. A quick look. 2. To take a quick look: He *glanced* around the room.

gradual (graj'ōō·əl) Happening slowly and in small steps; bit by bit. **gradually**

grandstand (grand'stand') The main seating place for people watching a ball game or other event.

guest (gest) 1. A person received or entertained by another, especially at a meal or party, or for a visit. 2. Someone who pays for a room, food, or both, in a hotel or inn.

H

harness (här'nis) Straps or bands used to hitch a horse or other animal to a cart, sled, and so on.

A harness

---

add, āce, câre, pälm; end, ēqual; it, īce; odd, ōpen, ôrder; tŏŏk, pōōl; up, bûrn; ə = a in *above*, e in *sicken*, i in *possible*, o in *melon*, u in *circus*; yōō — u in *fuse*; oil; pout

headdress (hed′dres′) A covering or decoration for the head.

hover (huv′ər) To remain in or near one place in the air, as with birds: The bird *hovered* over its nest.

I

impatient (im·pā′·shənt) **1.** Easily annoyed at having to wait, or for some other reason. **2.** Very eager: He was *impatient* to see his friend. **impatiently**

inland (in′lənd) Toward the inner part of a country; away from the shore: They traveled *inland*.

inn (in) A restaurant or hotel, usually by a roadside, for travelers.

international (in′tər·nash′ən·əl) Having to do with more than one nation, or with things between nations.

J

judge (juj) A person who decides a case in a court of law.

judgment (juj′mənt) The decision of the judge in a court of law.

K

kingdom (king′dəm) A country ruled by a King or Queen.

288

L

leggings (leg′ingz) Coverings for the leg.

limp (limp) To walk with an uneven step, as with a hurt leg or foot: After he fell, he *limped* all the way home.

log (lôg) **1.** Part of the trunk or a branch cut from a tree. **2.** A record kept every day of a ship's voyage.

M

mane (mān) The long hair growing on the neck of some animals, as the horse and lion.

A lion's mane

match[1] (mach) A small, thin piece of wood with a special tip that catches fire when rubbed against something rough.

match[2] (mach) **1.** To be alike or go with: The colors of the hat and coat *match*. **2.** A game or contest: He watched the tennis *match*.

meadow (med′ō) A low or even piece of grassy land.

mine[1] (mīn) The one or ones that belong to me: This ball is *mine.*

mine[2] (mīn) A place in the ground where men dig for coal, iron, or other minerals.

mineral (min′ər·əl) Anything found in nature that is not a plant or animal: Coal and salt are *minerals.*

moose (mōōs) A large animal of the deer family.

Moose, about 5 feet high at shoulder

N

native (nā′tiv) Someone born in a certain place or country.

O

operation (op′ə·ra′shən) **1.** An act done by a doctor to a patient to make him well. **2.** An activity or plan of activities for a special purpose.

outnumber (out′num′bər) To be greater in number than: The boys *outnumbered* the girls.

P

partner (pärt′nər) A person who does something with someone else; especially a person in business with another person.

party (pär′tē) **1.** A gathering of people for enjoyment. **2.** A group of people working or doing something together: The *party* of five men set sail.

patient (pā′shənt) **1.** Able to wait for someone or something without complaining or getting annoyed. **2.** Calm and understanding: He is a *patient* teacher. **3.** A person in the care of a doctor for sickness or injury.

payment (pā′mənt) Money paid for something: He made a *payment* on his car.

penguin (pen′gwin) A black and white bird having flippers instead of wings, webbed feet, and very short legs on which it can stand straight up: *Penguins* usually live near the South Pole.

---

add, āce, câre, pälm; end, ēqual; it, īce; odd, ōpen, ôrder; tŏŏk, pōōl; up, bûrn; ə = a in *above*, e in *sicken*, i in *possible*, o in *melon*, u in *circus*; yŏŏ = u in *fuse*; oil; pout

perch (pûrch) **1.** Any place for sitting or standing, especially if high: The bird flew down from its *perch*. **2.** To sit, stand, or place something on a perch: He *perched* on a ladder.

A perch

pioneer (pī′ə·nir′) One of the first people to come to live in a new country or area.

promotion (prə·mō′shən) A move to a higher class, grade, or position of importance: He was happy with his *promotion* to captain.

propeller (prə·pel′ər) A thing with turning blades used to pull or push a boat or plane through water or air.

A propeller

pueblo (pweb′lō) An adobe or stone building or group of buildings of the Indians of the southwest United States.

Pueblo

Q

quite (kwīt) Very. He was *quite* happy to go.

R

ranch (ranch) A large farm for raising herds of cattle or other animals. **ranches**

related (ri·lā′tid) **1.** Connected. **2.** Belonging to the same family or group.

rescue (res′kyōō) **1.** To save or free from danger or harm. **2.** A saving from danger, harm, and so forth: He came to our *rescue*. **rescuing**

S

satellite (sat′ə·līt) **1.** A body in space that moves around a planet or other larger body in space: The moon is a *satellite* of the earth. **2.** A man-made object in space, sent up by rocket, that moves around the earth or other body in space.

scarecrow (skâr'krō') A rough likeness of a man dressed in old clothes and put in a field to scare birds away from crops.

scene (sēn) 1. A certain place and everything in it that can be seen: It was a beautiful country *scene*. 2. The place and time in which a play or story is set.

shelter (shel'tər) Something that covers or protects from danger or bad weather.

shipwreck (ship'rek') Damage to or ruin of a ship at sea.

skim (skim) 1. To move quickly and lightly over or near the top of something: He *skimmed* over the water on his skis. 2. To read quickly in glances, without reading every word: He *skimmed* through the story in a few minutes. **skimming**

sleet (slēt) A mixture of rain with snow or hail.

slim (slim) Thin or slender, as with the human body: That woman is *slim*.

smoke (smōk) To treat meat with smoke as a way of preserving it. **smoked**

sound (sound) Deep, unbroken: He had a *sound* sleep. **soundly**

stall (stôl) 1. A place in a stable where a horse or cow is kept. 2. A small stand for showing or selling things, as in a market.

A flower stall

standstill (stand'stil') A stop.

statue (stach'oo) A likeness, as of a person or animal, made of wood, clay, or other material.

stretch (strech) 1. To reach out with a part of the body: He *stretched* his arms. 2. A large, unbroken area of one kind: He crossed the *stretch* of sand.

surrender (sə·ren'dər) To give up, as to an enemy.

T

tailor (tā'lər) A man who makes or repairs clothes.

toll (tōl) A charge, tax, or fee, as on a bridge, road, and so on: The driver stopped to pay the *toll*.

---

add, āce, câre, pälm; end, ēqual; it, īce; odd, ōpen, ôrder; took, pool; up, bûrn; ə = a in *above*, e in *sicken*, i in *possible*, o in *melon*, u in *circus*; yoo = u in *fuse*; oil; pout

tomahawk (tom′ə·hôk) A weapon that looks something like an ax, used by the Indians of North America.

A tomahawk

townspeople (tounz′pē′pəl) People who live in towns or in a particular town.

tramp (tramp) A person without a home who wanders around and begs for a living.

trial (trī′əl) **1.** The testing of a case before a court. **2.** Done or used to try out or test something: The new car made a *trial* run.

tropical (trop′i·kəl) Having to do with, or located in, the tropics, a hot, often humid, area of the earth.

tube (tōob) A tunnel or subway for cars, trains, and so forth.

U

urge (ûrj) To plead with or try to talk someone into doing something: He *urged* his mother to let him go. **urged**

V

volcano (vol·kā′nō) An opening in the earth's crust from which hot gases, lava, ashes, and so forth, are thrown up, forming a cone-shaped hill or mountain. **volcanoes**

A volcano

voyage (voi′ij) A trip or journey. **voyages**

W

weed (wēd) Any useless or troublesome plant.

wobble (wob′əl) To move or sway from side to side: The top *wobbled* as it slowed down. **wobbled, wobbling, wobbly**

wreck (rek) **1.** To undergo ruin, or great damage. **2.** To ruin or to cause great damage. **3.** Something that has been ruined or damaged.

Y

yarn (yärn) Any spun thread for use in weaving or knitting.

292

THE VOCABULARY

New words in this book are listed below. Most new words are introduced by the teacher before pupils meet them in this book. Those words which children can identify independently are designated as Attack Words. Words introduced at previous levels, except for a few special nouns, are repeated in *Ring Around the World*. Compound words made up of two known words are not identified as new words. Variant forms of familiar words are not listed when they are formed with suffixes or prefixes that have been taught. (See the accompanying Teacher's Edition for a further discussion of the vocabulary in the Primary Readers of THE BOOKMARK READING PROGRAM.)

Words appearing in the Glossary of *Ring Around the World* are indicated by a degree mark(°).

NEW WORDS

UNIT I

1. . . . .
----
2. . . . .
3. evening
4. rhyming
   impossible
5. . . . .
6. broth°
7. folk°
8. cabbage
9. cloth
10. . . . .
11. . . . .
----
12. although
    delicious
13. . . . .
14. enjoyment
    seriously
15. . . . .
16. . . . .
17. courthouse
    judge°
18. lose
19. . . . .
20. . . . .
21. payment°
22. . . . .
23. judgment°
24. won
25. . . . .
----
26. egret°
    bush

27. urged°
    chief°
28. . . . .
29. brought
    patient°
30. . . . .
31. . . . .
32. reward
33. . . . .
----
34. fortunes°
35. . . . .
36. bowed
37. . . . .
38. sew
39. . . . .
40. kingdom°
41. . . . .
42. . . . .
43. . . . .
44. heaven
45. . . . .
46. . . . .
47. . . . .
----
48. (*Poem*)
49. . . . .
----
50. . . . .
51. gradually°
    combined
    plaid
52. pattern
53. touch

schwa
accented
54. . . . .

UNIT II

55. . . . .
----
56. . . . .
57. Alaska
    disappoint
58. . . . .
59. . . . .
60. . . . .
61. caught
62. . . . .
63. moment
64. . . . .
65. whoa
66. . . . .
67. . . . .
----
68. tropical°
    Fiji
    islands
69. . . . .
70. . . . .
71. . . . .
72. trial°
73. prepares
74. Fijians
75. bowsprit°
    dangerous
    coral°
    reefs

76. (*Poems*)
----
77. Puerto Rico
    San Juan
    arrive
    International°
78. guests°
79. . . . .
80. . . . .
81. exclaimed°
    imagine
82. skis
83. . . . .
84. . . . .
85. . . . .
86. . . . .
----
87. . . . .
88. Eskimo
89. Mexican
90. African
    Bushongo
    square
91. . . . .
92. scene°
----
93. (*Poems*)
94. related°
    suffix
95. . . . .
96. . . . .
97. operate
    operation°

°Word in Glossary

258. ....
259. contented°
260. Sergeant
     admired°
261. ....
262. ....
263. ....

264. ....
265. customer
266. ....
267. ached°
268. June
269. ....
270. ....

271. ....
272. ....
273. ....
274. ....
275. toll°
276. carnation°
277. ....

278. ....
279. ....
280. ....
281. ....
282. ....

ATTACK WORDS

Pages 2–11
tramp°
inn°
begged
starved
roam
stir
beef
carrots
fact
quite°
bread
cheap°
coin

Pages 12–25
tailor°
joined
laughter
coat
owe
silver
case°
appear°
grabbed
rang
broke

Pages 26–33
cattle
gathered°
thorn
flew
perch°
cheer
throats
dig
beak
peck
less
peace
feeding

Pages 34–47
jolly

needle
thread
dreamed
sorry
sparrows
marry
neat
slept
drew
since
joy

Pages 50–54
braid
list

Pages 56–67
sled
chained
soup
brushing
checked
harness°
gee
haw
jerked
forward
trail
moose°
passed
tangled

Pages 68–75
copra°
coconut°
lamp
mat

Pages 77–86
cargo°
Christmas
north
baggage
hotel
gifts
ticket

licked
cream
puddle

Pages 87–92
stall°
inviting
carved°

Pages 94–98
fool
foolish
person
subtraction
contraction
decision
expansion
division
explanation
relation
realization

Pages 100–113
jail
crew
beads
bells
meat
cheese
weeks
weeds°
bunches
mine°
God
silk
candle
wore
cotton
parrots

Pages 114–120
explorer
beyond
built
fearless
wrecked°

except
twigs
camp
state

Pages 121–134
Thanksgiving
corn
crops°
straw
meal
Mayflower
drums
trumpet
led
shirt
stripe
Thee

Pages 136–143
boiled
unharmed
howdy
scalps
war
ain't
trick
warning
farther

Pages 144–148
frost°
forecasts
dollars
pray
rid
hail
outline

Pages 150–158
rubber
pillow
match°
porch
trap

fellow
bikes
choked
leaped
heel

Pages 159-171
sleet°
stretching°
nasty
trotted
poked
wobbling°
thumping
ordered

Pages 172–182
act
dragging
cabins
pine
ham

Pages 186–195
music
mamma
butt
gramma
swing
wiggle
daddy
hello
uncle
note
tune
swooped
giggling
main

Pages 196–200
unbutton

Pages 202–211
beam
stack
records

295

C 2
D 3
E 4
F 5
G 6
H 7
I 8
J 9